D1131540

Models of Change and Response Uncertainty

Prentice-Hall Series in Mathematical Analysis of Social Behavior

James S. Coleman and James March, Editors

Flament *Applications of Graph Theory to Group Structure*
White *An Anatomy of Kinship: Mathematical Models for Structures of Cumulated Roles*
Coleman *Models of Change and Response Uncertainty*

PRENTICE-HALL INTERNATIONAL, INC. London
PRENTICE-HALL OF AUSTRALIA, PTY., LTD. Sydney
PRENTICE-HALL OF CANADA, LTD. Toronto
PRENTICE-HALL OF INDIA (PRIVATE) LTD. New Delhi
PRENTICE-HALL OF JAPAN, INC. Tokyo

Models of Change and Response Uncertainty

James S. Coleman

Professor of Social Relations
The Johns Hopkins University

PRENTICE-HALL, INC. ENGLEWOOD CLIFFS, NEW JERSEY

Library of Congress Catalog Card Number 65-10329
Printed in the United States of America
C:58596

Preface

A few years ago, I became interested in the development of some means of studying the distributions of opinions in a population in a better way than had thus far been done. I was interested not merely in the distribution of overt responses, such as one finds in published polls and surveys, but in the distribution of persons themselves. For example, if 30 per cent of a population says "yes" in response to a question about whether China should be admitted to the U.N., how should this be interpreted in terms of the distribution of persons? Does it mean that there is a fixed 30 per cent of the population who believes this, with a fixed 70 per cent opposed? Or does it mean that *each* person in the population will respond this way about 30 per cent of the time, and give the opposite response about 70 per cent of the time? Obviously, the social consequences of these two distributions are very different. Just as obviously, one cannot tell which of these distributions (or what intermediate) is true from the single response alone. The response is confounded with the individual, and there is no way to separate the distribution of individuals from the distribution of responses. Two or more responses from the same individual are required.

The first developments arising out of this interest are contained in Chapter 12 of Coleman (1964). This approach is to take two responses by the same individual (to the same question on successive surveys, or to similar questions on the same survey) and, assuming that no change has occurred over time, to estimate the distribution of individuals between the two extremes of always responding "yes" and always responding "no."

This approach, however, led to difficulties, because change does occur, and thus what looks like a high amount of response uncertainty in a population may in fact be change of attitude that members of the population are undergoing. It became evident that in order to separate this response uncertainty at a given point in time from the change that is occurring through time, still a third response is necessary.

This led to examination of data that appeared to contain not only response uncertainty or change, but both. Most sociopsychological data that I have examined appear to show both these components, neither of which can be measured until the other is removed. The response uncertainty confounds simple models of change, such as Markov processes, and the change confounds simple treatments of reliability.

This book grew out of the attempt to separate these two elements by a model that explicitly incorporated both of them. As this developed, it became related to efforts to handle social data from multiwave panels, which does not conform to the general pattern of a Markov process. I decided, as a consequence, to take this general problem as the starting point of the analysis. Thus the history of this approach as it developed in my own work does not appear here. This has the serious defect that the problem with which the investigation began — the distributions of attitudes in populations — becomes obscured. The application of this model to this problem can provide a beginning to its study, but obviously it is only one tool for doing so. It has become evident, however, that if we are to study such problems, even more powerful mathematical tools will be necessary, as will more extended data from samples of individuals.

This work has profited particularly from the ideas of Lee Wiggins, who so far as I am aware was the first to develop models of attitude change in which the processes that occurred were among states that were only indirectly related to the response. Those who are familiar with the work of Paul Lazarsfeld will note also the similarity of the basic ideas in this model to the concept of "local independence" in latent structure analysis.

Work on this book has been greatly facilitated by Grant No. G25041 from the Social Sciences Division of the National Science Foundation for investigations into this problem, as well as by the freedom for research provided by The Johns Hopkins University.

JAMES S. COLEMAN

Contents

Models of Change and Response Uncertainty

CHAPTER ONE

Introduction to the Problem

1. An Empirical Regularity

In observing behavior of the same individuals at different times, a difficult problem of interpretation often arises. For unless a person responds in the same way each time he is observed, differences or variations in his responses must be accounted for. A major branch of psychology—learning theory—is devoted to explaining one kind of variation. In behavior described as learning, there is ordinarily some systematic direction of change, so that at the end of a period of time, the person appears to be in a state different from his original state. In such cases, the general term "learning" is used to describe the variation in response, implying that the observed variations represent a change in the individual's state. This term, of course, leaves open the question of how the change in state took place, and merely sets the problem, which learning theories in turn attempt to explain.

However, in many areas of behavior there are variations in response for which the term "learning" would hardly be appropriate. The most relevant notion in psychology is that of test-retest reliability. When individuals are given the same stimulus two or more times, some of them respond differently to it, even when the aggregate response frequency has not changed. For example, in the data of Table 1.1, the marginal frequencies remain about the same on the second observation as on the first, even though a large proportion of persons gave different responses on the two occasions.

Table 1.1. All adjacent pairs of purchases of pancake mix of brands 0, 1, 2 (from Fourt, 1960)

		Purchase 1			
		0	1	2	
	0	232	55	37	324
Purchase 0	1	50	213	59	322
	2	32	56	253	341
		314	324	349	987

In a case such as this, the interpretation implicit in the very concept of item reliability seems an appropriate one. This is the interpretation that responses are not a perfect measure of the individual's state. In effect, an individual is assumed to have only a given probability of making a particular response, and his sequence of responses merely measures this probability. His two or three or more responses are treated as if they were outcomes of throws of a biased coin.

These two extremes, learning and unreliability, are in effect extreme models or ideal types of behavior. The first is a model of individual change, the second a model of stable response uncertainty. But behavior is far more complex than either of these ideal types, and it is the complexity that provides the problem for this monograph. In particular, a wide range of data shows a certain empirical regularity, which neither of the extreme ideal types can explain. To make this more explicit involves specifying these ideal types further. Consider the data of Table 1.1. Probably the simplest model of change that is compatible with these data is a Markov process, in which the individual's states are 0, 1, and 2. The Markov process is defined by (a) a set of probabilities, p_{it}, representing the probability that the individual is in state i at time t, and (b) a set of transition probabilities, r_{ij}, representing the probability of change from state i to state j in the single time period between t and $t + 1$.

The equation describing the process for a given state i in a system of s states is:

$$p_{i,t+1} = \sum_{j=1}^{s} p_{jt} r_{ji} \tag{1.1}$$

Obviously, the sum of p_{jt} over j must equal 1, and the sum of the transition probabilities from state j ($\sum_i r_{ji}$) must equal 1. In the case of the three-state system of Table 1.1, the equations which carry the probabilities from t to $t + 1$ are:

$$\begin{aligned} p_{1,t+1} &= p_{1t}r_{11} + p_{2t}r_{21} + p_{3t}r_{31} \\ p_{2,t+1} &= p_{1t}r_{12} + p_{2t}r_{22} + p_{3t}r_{32} \\ p_{3,t+1} &= p_{1t}r_{13} + p_{2t}r_{23} + p_{3t}r_{33} \end{aligned} \tag{1.2}$$

With data of the sort shown in Table 1.1, the state probabilities are estimated merely by the marginal probabilities, and the transition probabilities by the internal cell frequencies divided by the row frequencies (see Anderson and Goodman, 1947, for further discussion of estimates). If n_{ij} is the number in row i and column j, $n_{i.}$ and $n_{.j}$ are the marginal frequencies in row i and column j, respectively, and n is the total number, the estimates are:

$$\hat{p}_{it} = n_{i.}/n \tag{1.3}$$

$$\hat{r}_{ij} = n_{ij}/n_{i.} \tag{1.4}$$

It is important to recognize the assumptions implicit in the use of Eq. (1.3) to estimate p_{it} and Eq. (1.4) to estimate r_{ij}. In both cases, the estimates are proportions taken over a reference class—for these data, a reference class of individuals. This involves the assumption that each individual is characterized by an identical process, with identical r_{ij}'s, and that the aggregate data represent the sum of n independent identical processes. Under such a circumstance, then, if p_{it} is the probability of any individual's being in state i at time t, and r_{ij} is the transition probability from state i to j, the expected values of the observed proportions $n_{i.}/n$ and $n_{ij}/n_{i.}$ are p_{it} and r_{ij}, respectively. Thus the observed proportions can be used as estimates of p_{it} and r_{ij}.

We will later raise the question of whether it is reasonable to assume that all individuals are characterized by identical processes. At this point, however, it is sufficient to note that in fitting a Markov process to a two-wave panel of a set of individuals where the state is assumed identical to the response, such an assumption is necessary. With these estimates, it is possible to carry the process forward (or backward) in time, to predict what the marginal frequencies will be for any time period in the future or past, and to predict what the internal cell frequencies would be for any cross tabulation between two or more time periods. In particular, the process would predict Table 1.2 for the cross tabulation between t and $t + 2$.

Table 1.2. Predicted cross tabulation between purchase 0 and purchase 2 from Markov process assumption

Purchase 0 (*time t*)	Predicted purchase 2 (*time t + 2*): 0	1	2	
0	178	82	64	324
1	74	159	89	322
2	55	84	202	341
	307	325	355	987

This table shows a difference from Table 1.1 characteristic of Markov processes applied to data in which there is a positive relation between the response at time t and $t + 1$.* The frequencies in the main diagonal decline as the number of time periods between observations increases. For time t vs. $t + 1$, the frequencies are 232, 213, 253; the predicted frequencies for time t vs. $t + 2$ are 178, 159, 202. Intuitively it is evident that as the time difference between the two observations increases, the positive relation between the observations will decrease.

The other extreme ideal type, involving response uncertainty, also gives rise to a prediction about the cross tabulation between times t and $t + 2$ on the basis of Table 1.1. If we assume that individual k has a probability v_{ik} of giving response i, then the expected proportion of responses in category i will be

$$E(n_{i.}/n) = \frac{1}{n}\sum_{k=1}^{n} = v_{ik} \tag{1.5}$$

This expected value may be estimated as the average of $n_{i.}/n$ and $n_{.i}/n$, since no change is assumed. Similarly, the expected proportion giving response i at time t and response j at another time, $t + \tau$, is the sum over individuals of the products

$$E(n_{ij}/n) = \frac{1}{n}\sum_{k=1}^{n} v_{ik}v_{jk} \tag{1.6}$$

This expected value may be estimated as the average of n_{ij}/n and n_{ji}/n, since $E(n_{ij}/n) = E(n_{ji}/n)$ from Eq. (1.6). For the data of Table 1.1, the predicted cross tabulation between t and $t + 2$ would be almost identical to Table 1.1,

* By "positive relation" is meant that the estimate of each transition probability in the main diagonal, r_{ii}, is greater than all others in that column.

differing only because of the adjustments necessary in averaging n_{ij}/n and n_{ji}/n. The table would be merely a replica of Table 1.1, except for these adjustments to make it symmetrical. Obviously, since in such a model there is no change at all, the time separating observations is irrelevant to the relationship observed between them in a cross tabulation. Thus the prediction would contrast sharply with that of the Markov process, where the relationship declines over time. Whereas the Markov process fitted to these data predicts a progressive reduction in the main diagonal, the model of response uncertainty predicts no decline at all.

Fortunately, there are a number of areas of behavior in which data have been gathered covering three or more responses of the same individuals. Thus these models, which give such different predictions, may be tested by examining the cross tabulations between observations separated by various periods of time.

In this example, the cross tabulation between t and $t + 2$ is given in Table 1.3.

Table 1.3. Actual cross tabulation between purchase 0 and purchase 2

		Purchase 2 (time + 2) 0	1	2	
Purchase 0 (time t)	0	218	65	41	324
	1	67	186	69	322
	2	33	56	252	341
		318	307	362	987

The data indicate that the frequencies in the main diagonal do decline, as the Markov process would imply—but the decline is much less than the Markov process predicts. The comparisons are

t vs. t + 1	*t vs. t + 2*		
	Actual	*Predicted (change)*	*Predicted (uncertainty)*
232	218	178	232
213	186	159	213
253	252	202	253

It is clear that the Markov process assumptions of change simply do not fit these data, nor do the response-uncertainty assumptions. Furthermore, almost without exception, behavioral data covering three responses of the same persons show similar results. The regularity is a striking one: the data nearly always fail to fit the model in the same way. There is decline in the main diagonal frequencies, but less decline than would be predicted from the Markov process, in which transition probabilities are estimated from time t vs. $t + 1$.

A little reflection will suggest why this occurs so frequently. Suppose people did change but were not perfectly homogeneous in their probabilities of shifting from state i to j, but some were more volatile, more likely to shift than others. Then the group of persons who actually did shift between time t and $t + 1$ would include a disproportionate number of these volatile persons, and the group that did not shift would contain a disproportionate number of the stable persons. Consequently, in predicting the number of these remaining persons who will shift, it is incorrect to apply a transition probability based on the total group that included the volatile persons. Such a calculation will overpredict change of the stable group and under-predict the change of those who have already made one shift. The end result would ordinarily be a discrepancy of the type found in the data above: an overprediction of the decline in the main diagonal.

Another way of looking at the behavior indicates the same thing, but from the perspective of response uncertainty. Suppose there is unreliability of response, so that each individual k is characterized by a probability v_{ik} of giving response i. But then suppose this probability itself undergoes some change through time. If so, then in the t vs. $t + 1$ table, the cell frequency n_{ij} (where $j \neq i$) is generated partly by the mere fact that some persons have at a given time a nonzero probability of responding to both i and j; that is, for a given individual k, $v_{ik}>0$ and $v_{jk}>0$. But it is increased also by the actual movement of some persons away from response i toward response j. Obviously, if the time span between observations is increased, there are likely to be more such people, since there will have been more movement, thus incrementing n_{ij} further, and decreasing n_{ii} further. Thus in the table t vs. $t + 2$, the value of n_{ii} will be less than in the table t vs. $t + 1$, though more than if the apparent shifts were due to change alone.

The kind of result shown in these data, which fall between the two ideal types, is found in a wide variety of behavioral data. In short-term occupational mobility, Blumen, Kogan, and McCarthy (1955) show this: the frequency of occupational shifts between time 0 and time 0 plus 3 months can be used to estimate transition probabilities between occupations. But the stability between time 0 and time 0 plus 12 months is greater than these transition probabilities would predict. The data fall between the Markov process model and the response uncertainty model.

In consumer behavior, the existence of consumer panels has provided a wide range of data that show the same pattern. Kuehn (1958) shows that in the successive purchases of frozen orange juice, shifting between brands shows the same behavior. Frank (1962) shows a similar result for purchases of coffee, and Table 1.4 a similar result for purchases among the eleven dominant brands of another grocery item.*

Table 1.4. Purchases of a grocery item from among eleven brands in the product class. (Upper table is pairs of purchases separated by three intervening purchases; lower table is pairs of purchases separated by seven intervening purchases)

		Brand of purchase x + 4											
		1	2	3	4	5	6	7	8	9	10	11	*Total*
Brand of purchase x	1	106	14	14	5	6	12	8	21	23	12	3	224
	2	16	50	3	4	1	1	1	4	6	1	2	89
	3	17	4	81	4	2	7	7	23	19	7	2	173
	4	7	2	4	48	8	2	5	16	15	1	1	109
	5	2	1	6	2	33	2	12	8	11	4	0	81
	6	14	0	7	3	1	15	4	2	7	3	3	59
	7	9	5	10	6	8	5	31	27	19	3	2	125
	8	8	2	17	10	5	5	6	159	10	7	1	230
	9	23	8	26	10	16	7	12	18	143	11	4	278
	10	8	0	4	0	3	4	2	8	5	30	3	67
	11	1	0	4	0	1	3	0	5	5	6	12	37
	Total	211	86	176	92	84	63	88	291	263	85	33	1472

		Brand of purchase x + 8											
		1	2	3	4	5	6	7	8	9	10	11	*Total*
Brand of purchase x	1	95	12	12	3	10	18	9	28	22	14	1	224
	2	16	45	3	5	1	4	2	5	6	1	1	89
	3	18	6	65	4	2	8	3	33	30	2	2	173
	4	5	4	9	49	5	3	5	15	9	5	0	109
	5	10	2	4	6	28	3	11	6	7	2	2	81
	6	14	1	7	1	1	15	2	2	11	2	3	59
	7	14	2	7	6	7	3	37	24	22	1	2	125
	8	9	2	15	13	5	4	13	154	7	5	3	230
	9	30	9	25	9	7	9	16	21	131	13	8	278
	10	7	0	8	1	1	0	1	11	4	34	0	67
	11	2	1	5	0	1	3	0	6	9	2	8	37
	Total	220	84	160	97	68	70	99	305	258	81	30	1472

* These data, which will be analyzed in some detail later, show an interesting deviation from this pattern when the 0–1 table is compared to the 0–2 table. In most cases, the main diagonal is *greater* in the 0–2 table. This result occurs because in the purchase of this item, more than one brand is used at the same time. Thus two brands are often purchased at the same time, or on successive store visits, making the adjacent purchases less often alike than purchases at one remove. To reduce this effect for this item, it is necessary to compare the 0–4 and 0–8 purchases, even though in the data of Table 1.4, multiple purchases on the same day are excluded by arbitrarily eliminating one.

Another set of data that show a similar result are cross tabulations of employment and unemployment of the same persons at different points in time. The data in Table 1.5 (from Levenson, 1963) show the employment of graduates of two vocational schools for four quarters after graduation. The second, third, and fourth quarters are tabulated against the first.

Table 1.5. Interquarter turnover in OASI-covered employment for first four quarters after graduation from high school.

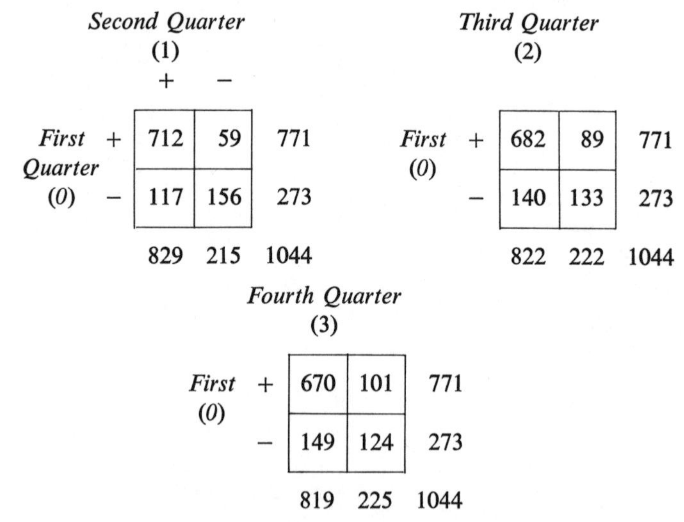

First Quarter (0)	Second Quarter (1) +	Second Quarter (1) −	
+	712	59	771
−	117	156	273
	829	215	1044

First (0)	Third Quarter (2) +	Third Quarter (2) −	
+	682	89	771
−	140	133	273
	822	222	1044

First (0)	Fourth Quarter (3) +	Fourth Quarter (3) −	
+	670	101	771
−	149	124	273
	819	225	1044

These data, as those of Table 1.4, show declining values of the main diagonal—but not as much decline as would be predicted by a Markov process model of the sort described earlier. Markov process calculations using the 0–1 table would show that the data in the 0–2 and 0–3 table simply do not fit—the main diagonals are too large. This is the kind of result that will occur if people do change, but have different probabilities of change: a few persons with high probabilities of becoming unemployed, and others with low probabilities.

Survey data, in multiwave panels, show a similar pattern in changes of attitudes. A Markov process calculation would make it evident that the data usually show the same empirical regularity: a decline in the main diagonal as the time period between interviews increases, but a decline which is less than that of a Markov process. The respondents are behaving as if they are not homogeneous in their probabilities of change, but some switch back and forth, while others are stable.

That this pattern of results is so frequent will not be puzzling if one stops to consider the assumptions of the two ideal types whose predictions straddle the empirical results. The application of a Markov process to such data implies that all persons are identical in their transition probabilities, a highly unrealistic assumption. Even if the Markov process assumptions were correct at all other points, any heterogeneity in the transition probabilities would produce such a pattern. Whatever behavior is measured, it is extremely unlikely that any set of persons would be identical in their transition probabilities.

Similarly for the response uncertainty model. Only if there were no change at all would there fail to be a decline in the main diagonal as the space between observations increased. So long as any change whatsoever occurred, then n_{ii} would decline over time, because the sum of the cross products $v_{ik,t}v_{ik,t+\tau}$ (where $v_{ik,t+\tau}$ is the probability of individual k giving response i at time $t + \tau$) will decline as $p_{ik,t+\tau}$ drifts away from $v_{ik,t}$.

The empirical regularity, together with the quite reasonable verbal explanations that can account for it, leads naturally to attempts to mirror the process that actually does occur. The attempts that have been made have been of four distinct varieties. A short exposition of each of these will form a context within which the present work can be located.

2. Models to Account for the Empirical Regularity

2.1. The m-th Order Markov Process and Higher Order Extrapolation

The most direct strategy to account for these data is the movement from a first order Markov process to an m-th order process. In an m-th order process, the new vector of state probabilities depends on the states for the preceding m time periods, rather than merely the single preceding time period. Thus in a second order process, the new vector of state probabilities depends on the preceding two periods. An m-th order process can be treated just like the first order process by defining the states of the process so as to incorporate the history of the individual. In the first order process, the state of the individual in the Markov process is equated with the observed response. But in a second order process the state can be defined as the last two responses. Thus in a behavior with two possible responses, 1 and 0, there would be not two, but four states: 11, 10, 01, 00. The transition matrix would look like this:

Time	1→1	1	0	0
0 1	2→1	0	1	0
↓ ↓				
1 1	r_{11}	r_{12}	0	0
1 0	0	0	r_{23}	r_{24}
0 1	r_{31}	r_{32}	0	0
0 0	0	0	r_{43}	r_{44}

Since the second response (time 1) is incorporated in both the initial and the final state, there are four transition probabilities that are necessarily zero, as indicated above. The other four can be estimated directly from the $2 \times 2 \times 2$ table, which cross tabulates the three time periods. The data from three observations are just sufficient to estimate the state probabilities and transition probabilities, so that the fit of the model can be tested only with four or more observations.

This approach can obviously be used with three-wave panels. There are, however, two questions: how well does it fit the data when predictions are made for a fourth and subsequent observation, and how satisfactory is it conceptually or substantively as a way of conceiving of the process? On both these grounds, the model fares rather poorly. The one explicit application of the model to behavioral data of which I am aware is that of Kuehn (1958), who shows that in purchases of frozen orange juice, a second order process is not sufficient. Even a third order process did not fully eradicate the tendency for the stable occupants of a given state to remain there on the next response more often than would be predicted. Purely on grounds of predictability, such a solution is clearly not very satisfactory.

On substantive or conceptual grounds, the solution is no more satisfactory. It does not incorporate the clues that appear in the data that suggest what is really happening. That is, the data suggest either that there is a mixture between response uncertainty and a process of change, or that there is a set of different Markov processes occurring, different persons having different transition probabilities. Instead, the m-th order process implies that a series of previous responses determines the next one. There is little reason to believe that previous responses, apart from the immediately preceding one, directly influence a subsequent response. But let us suppose that we could justify such a belief in the case of purchase behavior on the grounds that a memory trace remained from previous purchases extending back beyond the immediately preceding one. Even then this model is intellectually unrewarding, for it makes no attempt to develop a model of such a memory trace and thus to translate the individual's history into his present state. It is more like blind curve fitting, in which an increase in predictability of an extrapolation is sought through an increase in the number of points used. In fact, a rather direct and close analogy can be made between projections made from an m-th order Markov process and extrapolation of a curve using $m + 1$ points. The simplest extrapolation of a curve formed from data points is a linear one using the two preceding points. This is analogous to a first order Markov process, which also uses two points in time. The next addition is to use the three preceding points for extrapolation, and so on, just as in a second, third, and higher order Markov process, more and more of the past history is incorporated. This procedure is analogous also to the use of increasing powers of a power series in x to predict y:

$$y^{(1)} = a + b_1x$$
$$y^{(2)} = a + b_1x + b_2x^2$$
$$y^{(3)} = a + b_1x + b_2x^2 + b_3x^3$$
etc.

Little is learned by such blind extrapolation, and in most cases it appears that the resort to higher order Markov processes is not a useful step to take.

2.2. Introduction of Explanatory Variables

A second approach that has been taken to these data constitutes an attempt to reduce the heterogeneity. Implicitly it accepts the assumption that transition probabilities may differ for different individuals, and introduces independent variables or attributes to account for these differences.

The most straightforward way to introduce such independent variables requires shifting to a continuous time Markov process. (See Feller, 1957, for a discussion of such processes.) In an s-state system, the equations defining the process are of the form

$$\frac{dp_{it}}{dt} = q_{11}p_{1t} + q_{21}p_{2t} + \dots + q_{s1}p_{st} \tag{2.1}$$

The quantities q_{ij} may be termed "transition rates" (they are sometimes termed "transition intensities," but this is a rather awkward term), for they are somewhat analogous to the transition probabilities of a discrete time process.* The property of the q_{ij}'s that makes the continuous time process so useful is the fact that, unlike transition probabilities, they are unbounded from above. Thus the assumption of additive effects a_k of a set of independent attributes, $1, 2, \dots k, \dots$, upon the transition rate from state i to j is straightforward:

$$q_{ij} = a_1 + a_2 + \dots + a_k + \dots + a \tag{2.2}$$

where a is the residual component of q_{ij} due to other attributes not explicitly introduced.

This model can be used in conjunction with two-wave panel data whenever

* If the set of differential equations describing the continuous time process is integrated between time 0 and t, a set of equations results of the form

$$p_{1t} = r_{11t}p_{10} + r_{21t}p_{20} + \dots + r_{s1t}p_{s0}$$

where the r_{ijt}'s are functions of the q_{ij}'s and t. The r_{ijt}'s have exactly the properties of transition probabilities in a discrete time Markov process. Thus if a continuous time Markov process is in fact occurring, then a discrete time model may be used to describe it, provided that the time periods separating observations are equal. In other words, for each time period t in a given continuous time process, a particular discrete time Markov chain with transition probabilities r_{ijt} may be *embedded* in the process.

the individuals are characterized by other attributes. It thus differs from the other models discussed in this chapter, as well as from the one to be developed in subsequent chapters, all of which require a three-wave panel for estimation of parameters.

The details of solving for the q_{ij}'s, and for estimating the parameters of effect a_k may be found in Coleman (1964), and an example of this model's use to separate subgroups with different transition rates may be found in McDill and Coleman (1963).

The values of this approach are evident, for rather than attempting to gain predictability simply by knowledge of earlier responses, the model introduces other attributes. When they do in fact account for variation in the q_{ij}'s, they add to the understanding of the behavior, which is not true for the m-th order Markov process.

The defect of this model for data that show the regularity described earlier should also be evident. Even assuming that the behavior does conform to a Markov process with different transition rates (or probabilities) among different individuals, the success of the model depends on finding just those explanatory variables that fully account for this heterogeneity. This is likely to be rather difficult, since a great many variables would probably have to be introduced before the Markov predictions within all subgroups would be correct.

2.3. The Mover-Stayer Model

Another approach to this problem is based on a close look at the process that seems to be producing these data. In the earlier examination of data, it appeared that some persons were volatile, moving frequently from state to state, while others were less so. One way of formalizing this assumption is to develop a model for the extreme case, in which some fraction of persons are "stayers," who do not leave the state they are in, while others are "movers," according to a regular first order Markov process. The estimation task and the testing of the model thus require estimation of the number of stayers in each state and the matrix of transition probabilities for the movers.

Blumen, Kogan, and McCarthy (1955), who introduced this model, offer estimation procedures that allow prediction of the cross tabulation between any two time periods; Goodman (1961) presents several estimating procedures that give superior estimates. In all these methods, the data required are a cross tabulation between time t and $t + 1$ and time t and $t + m$. For example, in the Blumen, Kogan, and McCarthy data, the observations are quarterly, so that the t vs. $t + 1$ table cross tabulates occupations in adjacent quarters. The other table they use cross tabulates quarters separated by eight quarterly periods, that is, t vs. $t + 8$.

In a two-state case, there are exactly enough data to estimate parameters, and when s is greater than 2, there are excess data for estimation. In general, estimates for this model improve as m increases in the t vs. $t + m$ table. Intuitively this can be seen by the fact that as m increases, the number n_{ii} more closely approaches its minimum, comprised of the number of stayers in state i plus a number of movers based on independence between responses.

In effect, this approach formalizes the notion of heterogeneity among individuals in their transition rates, but in a very special way—by assuming two extreme types. The model takes one step away from the homogeneous Markov assumption by compressing the heterogeneity into these two extreme types.

This approach will allow a better fit to the data than the simple homogeneous Markov assumption. It also seems superior to the second order Markov process, for its structure seems more nearly to correspond to the structure that exists in behavior. However, there are certain data that it fits poorly (Goodman, 1961, and Converse, 1962), and there are certain *a priori* reasons why it would probably do so. Suppose, as this model does, that the defect of the simple Markov process for these data were due wholly to heterogeneity among transition rates. Even when this was true, the mover-stayer model would fit perfectly only under very special conditions—when there were only two extreme values for each transition probability: zero for the stayers, and a single value, r_{ij}, for the movers. Such a circumstance seems highly unlikely to occur in the real world.

2.4. Incorporation of Response Uncertainty into a Markov Process

The fourth approach to data of this sort has been to attempt to incorporate response uncertainty and a Markov process into the same model. A Markov process is assumed, each individual having identical transition probabilities but departing in another way from the preceding models. In those, the response made by the individual was identified with the state of the individual. Here, however, the state of the individual is treated as an unobservable, an underlying state that is only probabilistically related to the response. Lee Wiggins (1955) developed models of this sort, beginning with a basic model of unreliability. An example of Wiggins' models would be a two-category item, categories 1 and 0, with two underlying classes, a and b. In class a, the probabilities of responses 1 and 0 were p_{1a} and p_{0a} $(= 1 - p_{1a})$, respectively. Similarly, in class b, the probabilities of responses 1 and 0 were p_{1b} and p_{0b}, respectively. Under certain assumptions about the size of the classes or the probabilities of response (the usual assumption being $p_{1a} = p_{0b}$ and $p_{0a} = p_{1b}$), it is possible to estimate, in a two-wave panel, the other parameters.

Then with a third observation, the decline from $n_{ii,1}$ to $n_{ii,2}$ can be used to infer movement between the two classes according to a Markov process. Such movement will produce a decline in n_{ii}, so it was natural for Wiggins to superimpose a Markov process upon the basic response-unreliability model. In this way, a process was operating at the latent level and giving responses that only hazily reflected the process. Wiggins called these models "latent process models," and the name reflects their nature. The models are closely related to Lazarsfeld's (1959) latent structure analysis, for the underlying latent structure (of classes or a continuum) is the same, and the assumed relation of the classes to the observed data is the same.

Kuehn, in more recent work on consumer behavior (1962), has turned to similar models for describing sequences of purchases. He uses a Bush-Mosteller (1955) learning model, in which it is assumed that the individual's state is a probability of making a given response. The response itself (assumed to be followed by a reward or punishment) brings about an increase or a decrease in this probability. Thus a sequence of responses 1111 is not merely an *indicator* of being in a given state (as it would be in Wiggins' model), but has an effect in leading toward even greater probability of response 1 if the response is rewarded, or smaller probability if it is punished. This again is a Markov process, operating at a latent level, to change the underlying state (which is a probability) in discrete jumps toward 0 or 1.

Kuehn's model will account, as will Wiggins', for the declining value of n_{ii}, as t increases. But because of the estimation techniques developed for these learning models, they are most appropriate for sequences of responses of some length, rather than for a sequence of two or three responses from members of a large sample.

The conceptual differences between the Wiggins and Kuehn approaches are principally two. The first lies in the conception of the underlying latent states. For Wiggins, these are quite general, and are defined independently of the probability of making a given response. For example, if the model is one of a latent continuum, the relation between the continuum and the response probability for a given category may be an irregular curve, a step function, or even nonmonotonic. In Kuehn's model, the state is defined in terms of the probability of making a given response. For a two-response system, with categories 0 and 1, the state is defined by a single number, p_1, lying along the line segment 0.0 to 1.0. For a three-response system, 0, 1, 2, the state is defined by p_0 and p_1 (and p_2, which equals $1 - p_0 - p_1$), and lies in a plane that is an equilateral triangle.

The second difference between Wiggins' models and those of Kuehn lies in the conception of the role of the response. In Kuehn's model, the response itself, and the subsequent reward or punishment, determines what transition probability is operative to move the individual into a new state. In Wiggins' models, the responses are mere indicators of the underlying state, and the change proceeds independently of the response.

It is likely that some kinds of behavior fit this assumption of Wiggins', while other kinds fit the assumption of Kuehn's. Clearly, learning experiments are often constructed so that the response is rewarded or punished and thereby has an effect, as Kuehn's model assumes. But in other behavior, in natural settings, it is less clear. Especially in items used in questionnaires or interviews, the response is ordinarily treated as an indicator of an underlying state that is subject to change from various factors, but little affected, if at all, by the response itself.

The model to be developed in subsequent chapters lies within this fourth approach, which combines ideas of response uncertainty with a Markov process. It is most like Kuehn's model with respect to the first difference between Kuehn and Wiggins: it defines the state of the individual in a way that is directly related to the response probabilities. It is most like Wiggins', however, with respect to the second difference: it treats the response as an indicator of the individual's state rather than an independent determinant of it. But the development of this model is the topic of the next chapter, and discussion of it will proceed there.

3. Conclusion

The problem set by this chapter is wholly an empirical one: a data regularity that pervades a wide range of behavior and one unaccounted for by simple models of behavior, such as a simple Markov process. The four directions of work that have developed to account for this regularity have not been wholly satisfactory, and it is unlikely that any parsimonious model will be so. However, the approach that combines response uncertainty with a Markov process seems of interest, because it appears very likely that both properties are present in data of the sort described in this chapter.

CHAPTER TWO

The Study of Change in the Presence of Response Uncertainty

1. A Latent Markov Process Within the Individual

In development of a model that incorporates both response uncertainty and change, it is necessary to be able to measure both for any set of data that exhibits both. However, to partition the task, we will first examine the process and measurement of change, and only in a subsequent chapter will we examine the measurement of uncertainty. Thus in the present chapter, the intent is to show how we can measure change, having extracted the variation due to response uncertainty. Only later will we stop to examine the response uncertainty thus extracted.

Rather than conceiving of a process operating at the level of an individual, let us suppose that the unit which undergoes change is a *response element*, and that each individual has a large set of m such elements. Each of these elements is conditioned to, or associated with, a particular response. Considering the general case of s responses, there are $m_1, m_2, \ldots, m_s$ response elements associated with responses 1, 2, . . ., s, respectively. These response elements determine behavior in the following way. If $Pr\{R_i\}$ is the probability of giving response i, then

$$Pr\{R_i\} = \frac{m_i}{\sum_{j=1}^{s} m_j} \tag{1.1}$$

The process of change that we postulate for each element is a continuous time stochastic process between the states 1, 2, . . ., s. It is the simplest such process possible, for it is Markovian, and the transition rates are constant over time. If a simple discrete time Markov process is defined for infinitesimally small periods in time, dt, and the transition probability from state i to j for each period is $q_{ij}dt$, then the q_{ij}'s (for all $j \neq i$) are transition rates in a continuous time Markov process. It is this kind of process that we postulate for the elements, each element having a transition rate q_{ij} from each state i to each other state j. (The term "transition intensity" is often applied to the q_{ij}'s in the continuous time process. Because the term "transition rate" seems more felicitous, it will be used throughout this monograph.) If the probability of an element's being in state i at time t is v_{it}, then for a set of s possible states of the element, each element's behavior is governed by the system of equations

$$\begin{aligned}
\frac{dv_{1t}}{dt} &= q_{11}v_{1t} + \dots + q_{i1}v_{it} + \dots + q_{s1}v_{st} \\
&\vdots \\
\frac{dv_{it}}{dt} &= q_{1i}v_{1t} + \dots + q_{ii}v_{it} + \dots + q_{si}v_{st} \\
&\vdots \\
\frac{dv_{st}}{dt} &= q_{1s}v_{1t} + \dots + q_{is}v_{it} + \dots + q_{ss}v_{st}
\end{aligned} \tag{1.2}$$

Here the q_{ij}'s are transition rates for the elements; and q_{ii} is defined as $-\sum_{j=1}^{s} q_{ij}$. The solution of this system of differential equations is given by

$$\begin{aligned}
v_{1t} &= v_{10}r_{11t} + v_{20}r_{21t} + \dots + v_{s0}r_{s1t} \\
&\vdots \\
v_{st} &= v_{10}r_{1st} + v_{20}r_{2st} + \dots + v_{s0}r_{sst}
\end{aligned} \tag{1.3}$$

where r_{ijt} is a function of the q_{ij}'s and t. The quantities r_{ijt} have the properties of transition probabilities that carry forward the values of $v_1, \dots, v_s$ from time 0 to time t. They are specific to the time period t, and as t increases,

r_{ijt} increases when $i \neq j$, and decreases when $i = j$. Thus as time continues, each v_j becomes less dependent upon its original value and more dependent on values of other v_i's. The function that relates r_{ijt} to the q_{ij}'s is an infinite series, the first four terms of which are

$$r_{ijt} = \delta_{ij} + tq_{ij} + \frac{t^2}{2}\sum_{k=1}^{s} q_{ik}q_{kj} + \frac{t^3}{3!}\sum_{k=1}^{s}\sum_{h=1}^{s} q_{ik}q_{kh}q_{hj} + \ldots \tag{1.4}$$

where δ_{ij} is the Kroneker delta, 0 if $j \neq 1$, 1 if $j = i$. This result may alternatively be expressed in matrix notation

$$V_t' = V_0' e^{Qt} \tag{1.5}$$

where e^{Qt} is a matrix that is the sum of the infinite series

$$e^{Qt} = I + Qt + \frac{Q^2t^2}{2!} + \frac{Q^3t^3}{3!} + \ldots \tag{1.6}$$

Equation (1.6) is the matrix analog of an exponential series, and each term in the matrix is the sum r_{ijt}, as shown in Eq. (1.4).

Equations (1.2) define the probability of change for each of the m elements, so we have m independent identical processes governed by the same system of equations.* Consequently, v_{it} is also the expected proportion of elements conditioned to response i. This means that

$$v_{it} \approx Pr\{R_i\} = \frac{m_{it}}{\sum_{j=1}^{s} m_{jt}} \tag{1.7}$$

and thus by Eq. (1.1), v_{it} is the probability that this person will give response i at time t. (It is interesting to note what exists at the other extreme from the case of an arbitrarily large number of elements. In the case of *one* element, the model reduces to a simple Markov process at the individual level.)

The device of "response elements" is not strictly necessary, but it is perhaps the simplest way conceptually to use a model of qualitative change among states for characterizing the quantitative change of an individual. At the level of the elements, the change is among a set of s discrete states; but at the individual level, this becomes merely small steps in a space of $s - 1$ dimensions, and because of the large number of elements, it is in effect movement through a continuous space. In the case of two response categories, the movement of each element is from one state to the other; but the resulting movement of the individual consists of very small steps (or approximately continuous movement) along the line segment between zero and one. Thus

* As defined in Eq. (1.2), the m processes are independent. However, this is a simplification that will be rectified in Chap. 4, where the possibility of interdependence between the m elements will be discussed. However, the introduction of such a complication would not change the present section, and it is reserved until later.

the model is a special type of random walk in $s - 1$ dimensions with reflecting (rather than absorbing) barriers. But rather than observing the precise location of the individual engaged in the random walk (as, for example, the physicist does in the study of Brownian motion), we observe a qualitative response that depends probabilistically on his location. Only because the response is observed for a number of individuals, or for the same individual at many times, is it possible to measure the change at all. Because we have assumed m to be arbitrarily large, we look only at the expected movement of the individual, and his expected location $(v_{it}, \ldots, v_{s-1,t})$.

2. Aggregation and Estimation of Parameters

The empirical problem is to use the data on a sample of individuals or on a long sequence of responses from one individual, which consists of frequencies or proportions, to infer the transition rates at the level of elements within the individual. In the previous section, these transition rates were related to a probability at the level of the individual. Thus the remaining requirement is to relate the individual probability, v_{it}, to the proportion of persons who give response i.

Observations allow calculation of "the proportion of responses that are response i," where the proportion is formed by aggregating over individuals at a given point in time, or over time for a given individual. If this proportion were treated as an estimate of a probability associated with an individual in the reference class, there would be no problem. The task, however, is to use the empirical observations of proportions to estimate the q_{ij}'s, *without* assuming these proportions to be probabilities that characterize the individual. As Eq. (1.4) shows, the q_{ij}'s are functions of the r_{ijt}'s, and as shown in the appendix, they may be calculated from the r_{ijt}'s. Thus the task becomes one of using the observations to estimate the values of r_{ijt}.

For concreteness, we will assume that the class over which the proportion is taken is a set of individuals observed at a given time. If the proportions were taken over one individual's responses through time, the exposition below would not change except for the necessary change in interpretation.

If there are s responses, then each individual's state may be specified by an s-dimensional vector $(v_1, v_2, v_3, \ldots, v_{s-1}, t)$. (The value of v_s is dependent on the values of $v_1, \ldots, v_{s-1}$, since the v's sum to 1.0.) The set of individuals is specified by a frequency distribution in s dimensions, $f(v_1, v_2, \ldots, v_{s-1}, t)$. (The frequency distribution is normalized to equal 1.0 when summed over the entire space.) If the frequency distribution is specified at time t, then the expected frequency of individuals at position v_i at time t giving response i is

$$frv_i(R_i) = v_i f(v_i, t) \tag{2.1}$$

where $f(v_i, t)$ is the marginal distribution of individuals with respect to v_i. However, since we cannot identify separately the individuals at a given position v_i, we are interested in the sum of these expected frequencies over all values of v_i, to give the expected proportion of all individuals who give response i at time t. Representing the sum in Eq. (2.1) by an integral over v_i, we obtain

$$p_{i_t} = \int_0^1 v_i f(v_i, t)\, dv_i \tag{2.2}$$

where p_{i_t} is the expected proportion of individuals giving response i at time t.

This links together for the first time a quantity that can be estimated from observations, p_{i_t}, to the unobserved quantities v_{it}. It is necessary, however, to obtain a relation between the p_{i_t}'s, which can be estimated from the n_i's, and the unobserved quantities r_{ijt} in order to solve for the values of r_{ijt}. This may be done by specifying the expected frequency of response at v_i at time t, as a function of the frequency distribution of v_i at time t_0, $f(v_1, v_2, \ldots, v_{s-1}, t_0)$. Since there has been some movement between time 0 and time t, and consequently v_i at time t will depend on $v_1, v_2, \ldots, v_{s-1}$ at time 0, it is necessary to specify the total, rather than merely the marginal, distribution.

By substituting from Eq. (1.3) and integrating over the space, the expected frequency distribution is obtained in terms of r_{ijt} and the values of v_i at time 0.

$$p_{i_t} = \int_0^1 \cdots \int_0^1 (v_{10} r_{1it} + \ldots v_{s0} r_{sit}) f(v_1, \ldots, v_{s-1}, t_0)\, dv_1 \ldots dv_{s-1} \tag{2.3}$$

However, when the values of v_i are referred to the same time point as the frequency distribution, Eq. (2.2) may be used, and thus Eq. (2.3) reduces to

$$p_{i_t} = p_{1_0} r_{1it} + \ldots + p_{i_0} r_{iit} + \ldots + p_{s_0} r_{sit} \tag{2.4}$$

Equation (2.4) gives a desired relation between expected proportions p_{it}, of which observed proportions giving response i are an estimate, and the quantities r_{ijt}, from which the values of q_{ij} may be calculated. There are $s(s - 1)$ independent values of r_{ijt} in a system with s possible states of the elements. This requires at least an equal number of equations in order to obtain estimates. For each pair of times separated by time t, there are $s - 1$ independent equations of the form of Eq. (2.4). This means that the minimum number of observation points is $s + 1$, to provide s pairs of times, each pair separated by the same time period t. In particular, three equally spaced observations are required for estimating r_{10t} and r_{01t} in a dichotomy, where the possible responses are 1 and 0.*

The use of a sequence of $s + 1$ equally spaced observations in conjunction with Eq. (2.4) requires no use of the internal cells of a cross tabulation, and thus does not require observations on the same individuals. The values r_{ijt} can be estimated from separate samples. However, if the system is at or near statistical equilibrium, there will be little change in the values of p_{i_t} over time, and thus too little variation to obtain stable estimates of r_{ijt}. Ordinarily, a system that is far from equilibrium but undisturbed by exogenous factors is necessary in order to use Eq. (2.4) for the estimates of r_{ijt}. This may be seen for the dichotomous case in Eqs. (4.3) and (4.4) below.

More accurate estimates may be obtained, even when the system is at or near statistical equilibrium, by using the internal cell frequencies in a multi-wave panel. The minimum number of observations is three, but they need not be equally spaced.

The use of internal cell frequencies depends upon obtaining some relation between expected proportions of those who gave response i at time 0 and response j at time t (to be labelled $p_{i_0j_t}$), and the quantities r_{ijt}. If this were a standard Markov process, in which we treated observed proportions as estimates of probabilities, the matter would be simple: $p_{i_0j_t}/p_{i_0}$ would be an estimate of r_{ijt}. However, because $p_{i_0j_t}$ is treated as a proportion and nothing more, it must be defined in terms of the underlying v_i's. By use of considerations like those that led to Eq. (2.2), we obtain

$$p_{i_0j_t} = \int_0^1 \cdots \int_0^1 v_{i0}v_{jt}f(v_1, \ldots, v_{s-1}, t_0)\,dv_1, \ldots dv_{s-1} \tag{2.5}$$

That is, $p_{i_0j_t}$ is the sum of all the cross products of v_i at time 0 and v_j at time t. In the case of $p_{i_0i_t}$, this cross product would be v_i^2 if there were no movement in v, no shifting of the elements between states. Thus $p_{i_0i_t}$ would be independent of time; there would be no decline in $p_{i_0i_t}$ as t increased. This would be the circumstance assumed in test-retest reliability, where there is an implicit assumption that $p_{i_0i_t}$ is relatively insensitive to the time interval t.

It is possible to use Eq. (2.5) as an aid in estimating r_{ijt}, in conjunction with three observations, at times labelled 0, 1, and 2, with time period τ between observations 0 and 1, and t between observations 1 and 2.

Using Eq. (1.3) to obtain v_{i2} as a function of v_{i1}, and substituting in Eq. (2.5) gives

* Equation (2.4) is identical in form with the comparable equation for an individual-level Markov process, which identifies proportions with probabilities. Thus if marginal frequencies only are used to calculate the r_{ijt}'s, this model gives the same results as an ordinary Markov process. It is only in exceptional circumstances, however, that estimation can be based on marginal frequencies. Both in the ordinary Markov process and in this process, the usual estimation is based on internal cell frequencies.

$$p_{iоj_2} = \int_0^1 \cdots \int_0^1 v_{io}(v_{11}r_{1jt} + v_{21}r_{2jt} + \ldots + v_{s1}r_{sjt})$$

$$f(v_1, \ldots, v_{s-1}, t_0)\, dv_1 \ldots dv_{s-1} \tag{2.6}$$

An intuitive notion of what Eq. (2.6) expresses is given by considering the first term under the integral. The quantity $v_{11}r_{1jt}$ is the probability that an element was in state 1 at time 1 and j at time 2 (t = time 2 − time 1). Thus $v_{io}v_{11}r_{1jt}$ is the probability that an element is in state i at time 0, times the probability that the element is in state 1 at time 1 and state j at time 2. The equation may be reduced to a series of terms of the form of Eq. (2.5) and then reduced to

$$p_{ioj_2} = p_{io1_1}r_{1jt} + p_{io2_1}r_{2jt} + \ldots + p_{ios_1}r_{sjt} \tag{2.7}$$

Thus the expected proportion of individuals giving response i at time 0 and j at time 2 can be expressed as a function of the r_{ijt}'s and the expected proportions giving response i at time 0 and 1, 2, . . ., s at time 1. In a sequence of three observations on a set of individuals, the observed proportions giving response i at time 0 and j at time 2 are estimates of the expected value p_{ioj_2}, and the observed proportions giving response i at time 0 and 1, 2, . . ., s at time 1 are estimates of the expected values $p_{io1_1}, p_{io2_1}, \ldots, p_{ios_1}$. Thus such data are usable, in conjunction with Eq. (2.7), to estimate the values of r_{ijt}. There are s independent equations for $p_{1oj_2}, p_{2oj_2}, \ldots, p_{soj_2}$, which involve these same parameters, $r_{1jt}, r_{2jt}, \ldots, r_{sjt}$. These equations may be solved by the usual means for solution of simultaneous equations. There are s sets of such equations (only $s - 1$ independent sets), and these may be similarly solved to give estimates of all r_{ijt}'s. It should be noted that the values of r_{ijt} are relative to the time period between the observations at times 1 and 2. The time period between times 0 and 1 plays no part in the calculation.

Equation (2.7) is the crucial equation for relating the observed data to the transition probabilities r_{ijt}, for the observed data in the 0–1 cross tabulation give proportions that are estimates of p_{ioj_1}, and the observed data in the 0–2 cross tabulation give proportions that are estimates of p_{ioj_2}. With these data and Eq. (2.7), it becomes possible to solve for the values of r_{ijt} by solving successive sets of simultaneous equations. That is, for each row of r_{ijt}'s in the transition matrix, we have s equations of the form of Eq. (2.7):

$$p_{1oj_2} = \sum_{i=1}^{s} p_{1oi_1}r_{ijt} \tag{2.8}$$

$$\vdots$$

$$p_{soj_2} = \sum_{i=1}^{s} p_{soi_1}r_{ijt}$$

These s equations can be solved to give estimates of the s transition probabilities in column j, $r_{1jt}, \ldots, r_{sjt}$. Altogether, s such sets of equations can be formed, and their solution gives the matrix of transition probabilities, r_{ijt}.

Having these estimates of r_{ijt}, it is then possible to obtain estimates of the values of q_{ij}, using Eq. (1.4). Computational methods for both these tasks are described in the appendix.

For those familiar with operations on matrices, Eq. (2.8) may be expressed in matrix form:

$$P(0,2) = P(0,1)R(t) \tag{2.9}$$

where $P(0, 2)$ is an $s \times s$ matrix with elements $p_{i_0j_2}$, $P(0, 1)$ is an $s \times s$ matrix with elements $p_{i_0j_1}$, and $R(t)$ is an $s \times s$ matrix with elements r_{ijt}. Premultiplying both sides of Eq. (2.9) by the inverse of $P(0, 1)$ gives

$$P(0,1)^{-1}P(0,2) = P(0,1)^{-1}P(0,1)R(t) \tag{2.10}$$

and since the product of a matrix times its inverse gives the identity matrix, this reduces to

$$P(0,1)^{-1}P(0,2) = R(t) \tag{2.11}$$

Thus by finding the inverse of $P(0, 1)$ and premultiplying $P(0, 2)$ by this inverse, we find $R(t)$.

2.1. Estimation of the Equilibrium Distribution

The transition probabilities, r_{ijt}, for the process allows estimation of the equilibrium distribution of p_i. The equilibrium distribution is by definition a distribution of p_{i_e} such that Eq. (2.4) becomes

$$p_{i_e} = p_{1_e}r_{1it} + \ldots + p_{i_e}r_{iit} + \ldots + p_{s_e}r_{sit} \tag{2.12}$$

whatever the time period t over which r_{ijt} is defined. That is, when the matrix of transition probabilities is imposed as an operator on the values of p_{i_e}, the resulting distribution is identical to the initial one.

The set of Eqs. (2.12) can be solved for the values of p_{i_e}, since there are $s - 1$ independent equations, and $s - 1$ independent values of p_{i_e} (one is constrained by the fact that the sum of p_{i_e} equals 1.0). This is done by first transposing p_{i_e} so that the equations become

$$0 = p_{1_e}r_{1it} + \ldots + p_{i_e}(r_{iit} - 1) + \ldots + p_{s_e}r_{sit} \tag{2.13}$$

Then, by successive elimination, using the first $s - 1$ equations, the value of p_{s-1_e} can be found, and by successive resubstitution in the intermediate equations, the other values may be found.

3. Expected Movement of the Individual

Because the transition rate q_{ij} and the transition probability r_{ijt} are specified in terms of a process at the level of elements within the individual, it is necessary to inquire how to interpret a given value of q_{ij} or r_{ijt} in terms of change of the individual. That is, individuals at time 1 are at different points in the space of $s - 1$ dimensions, and at time 2 (= time 1 + t) there will have been some change in their positions. This change will, of course, depend not only upon the values of q_{ij} and t, but also upon the initial position of that individual. Because we conceive of the individual as an aggregate of m elements, each described by the same equation, then Eq. (1.3) is a differential equation for changes in the *expected* state of the individual. Thus since at the level of the individual we no longer treat the process stochastically, but look only at the expected state, our interest is in the expected movement of the individual. In effect, for an individual whose initial position is specified, we will want to know what will be the expected amount of change in v_1, $v_2, \ldots, v_s$, between times 1 and 2. This can be determined from Eq. (1.3), by subtracting v_{i1} from both sides of the equation for v_{i2}:

$$\Delta v_{1t} = v_{12} - v_{11} = v_{11}(r_{11t} - 1) + v_{21}r_{21t} + \ldots + v_{s1}r_{s1t} \qquad (3.1)$$

$$\vdots$$

$$\Delta v_{st} = v_{s2} - v_{s1} = v_{11}r_{1st} \qquad + v_{21}r_{2st} + \ldots v_{s1}(r_{sst} - 1)$$

Thus by use of Eq. (3.1) it is possible to express the expected change in position for each individual, given his initial position. This can be illustrated for the simple case of two states, labelled 1 and 0, with transition probabilities r_{10t} and r_{01t}. (Here, as elsewhere when examining two-state systems, the states will be labelled 1 and 0, rather than 1 and 2. The special usefulness of this notation will arise later in the study of systems of dichotomies using binary numbers for notational convenience.) The change in position along the line segment v_1, between 0.0 and 1.0 is

$$\begin{aligned}\Delta v_{1t} &= v_{11}(r_{11t} - 1) + v_{01}r_{01t}\\ &= -v_{11}r_{10t} + (1 - v_{11})\, r_{01t}\\ &= r_{01t} - v_{11}(r_{01t} + r_{10t})\end{aligned}$$

For various values of v_{10}, in the case where $r_{10t} = r_{01t} = 0.2$:

v_{11}	Δv_{1t}
1.0	− 0.20
0.8	− 0.12
0.6	− 0.04
0.5	0.00
0.4	+ 0.04
0.2	+ 0.12
0.0	+ 0.20

In this case, the expected change, Δv_{1t}, is toward the mean of v_1, 0.5, and proportional to the distance from the mean. If $r_{10t} = 0.2$ and $r_{01t} = 0.3$, the expected changes would look like this:

v_{11}	Δv_{1t}
1.0	− 0.20
0.8	− 0.10
0.6	0.00
0.5	+ 0.05
0.4	+ 0.10
0.2	+ 0.20
0.0	+ 0.30

In general, the expected changes in v_i will depend upon the value of v_i at time 1, and upon the transition probabilities, r_{jit}. If v_i is above its mean, then the expected movement will be negative; if v_i is below its mean, the expected movement will be positive.

This fact seems at first glance paradoxical. The frequency distribution, $f(v_1, \ldots v_{s-1}, t_1)$ may be at equilibrium, yet the expected movement of any individual who is away from the mean is toward the mean. This would seem to bring about a collapsing of the distribution to a single point, at the mean. The reason this is not so may be found by considering an individual at point v_1^*, greater than the mean. His expected movement is down, toward the mean. However, this expected movement also has a variance. Due to this variance, for a given expected movement Δv_{1t}, some persons will move down and others up. Thus some persons who begin above the mean will in fact end even further above it, although their expected movement is down. In particular, at the mean itself, where the expected movement is zero, the existence of a nonzero variance of Δv_{1t} means that almost all persons will move away from the mean.

To give the equation for this variance would require knowledge of the probability distribution of individuals at any time t, given the initial position specified at point $v_1, v_2, \ldots v_s$ at time 0. It is likely that such a distribution would be similar to diffusion equations involving drift in the study of Brownian motion in physics. However, the study of such probability distributions is beyond the scope of this book, and the problem awaits further treatment.*

In any case, knowledge of this distribution is not necessary for examining

* In particular, I conjecture that the equation for the probability distribution in one dimension is identical to that developed for the change in genetic composition of a population characterized by two alleles, a and a'. When there are m_1 individuals with allele a, and $m - m_1$ with allele a', the population is to be characterized by a single parameter, $\gamma = m_1/m$. The probability distribution of γ_t after a given time t (assuming that m is large enough to treat γ as a continuous variable) has been studied by Feller (1951).

the empirical problem at hand, nor do the data available allow the empirical study of such distributions. The general question of the location of individuals in the space $v_1, v_2, \ldots, v_{s-1}$ (but not of their precise change in position) will be treated in Chap. 4.

It is possible here, however, to say something more about the expected movement of individuals, given particular values for r_{ijt}. It would be useful to calculate the amount of net change and the average amount of change for all individuals, regardless of direction, which will be called the gross change. This does not include the various back-and-forth movements that an individual might make in the continuous time process, but only the change represented by the difference between his original position and his final one. In terms of the notation used above, the gross change is the sum of the absolute values of Δv_{it} over all individuals.

The amount of net change is obtained very simply by summing Δv_{it} over all values of v_i. If the net change in dimension i is labelled Δc_i, then it is given by:

$$\Delta c_{it} = \int \ldots \int \Delta v_{it} f(v_1, \ldots, v_{s-1}, t_1)\, dv_1 \ldots dv_{s-1} \tag{3.2}$$

and using Eq. (3.1) gives

$$= \int_0^1 \ldots \int_0^1 (v_{11} r_{1it} + \ldots + v_{i1}(r_{iit} - 1) + \ldots + v_{s1} r_{sit})$$

$$f(v_1, \ldots, v_{s-1}, t_0)\, dv_1 \ldots dv_{s-1}$$

Integrating this equation gives

$$\Delta c_{it} = p_{1_1} r_{1it} + \ldots + p_{i_1}(r_{iit} - 1) + \ldots + p_{s1} r_{sit} \tag{3.3}$$

The right side of Eq. (3.3) is almost equal to that of Eq. (2.4), which defines $p_{i,t}$. Thus using Eq. (2.4) for times 1 and 2 gives

$$\Delta c_{it} = p_{i_2} - p_{i_1} \tag{3.4}$$

Thus the net change in individuals with respect to a given dimension i is reflected directly in the change in the marginal proportions, as in the regular Markov process, where the change is directly observed.

In a regular Markov process, in which observations are made on two successive time periods, the gross change is reflected directly by the sum of the off-diagonal cells in the turnover table. In the latent Markov process, however, the sum of $|\Delta v_{it}|$ requires knowledge of the distribution of individuals over the space. We know that below the mean of the equilibrium distribution of v_i, $\bar{v}_i$, the expected movement is positive, and above the mean it is negative, so that we can write (using the dichotomous case for simplicity):

$$\sum |\Delta v_{1t}| = \int_0^{\bar{v}} \Delta v_{1t} f(v_1)\, dv_1 - \int_{\bar{v}}^1 \Delta v_{1t} f(v_1)\, dv_1 \tag{3.5}$$

However, to carry out this integration and express it in terms of p_{1_t} and p_{1o1t} seems to require knowledge of the form of the distribution. Thus knowledge of $|\Delta v_{it}|$ must await Chap. 4, where a particular form for the distribution is assumed.

However, it is possible to calculate a measure of the gross change without knowledge of the form of the distribution. The sum of the squared expected movement, $\Sigma\,\Delta v_{it}^2$, can be calculated.

$$\sum \Delta v_{it}^2 = \int_0^1 \cdots \int_0^1 (v_{i2} - v_{i1})^2 f(v_1, \ldots v_{s-1}, t)\, dv_1 \ldots dv_{s-1} \tag{3.6}$$

Expanding the squared term gives

$$\sum \Delta v_{it}^2 = \int_0^1 \cdots \int_0^1 (v_{i2}^2 - 2v_{i2}v_{i1} + v_{i1}^2) f(v_1, \ldots v_{s-1}, t)\, dv_1 \ldots d_{s-1} \tag{3.7}$$

This equation reduces directly to

$$\sum \Delta v_{it}^2 = p_{i_2i_2} - 2p_{i_1i_2} + p_{i_1i_1} \tag{3.8}$$

Thus the sum of the squared expected movement may be found by use of the observed values of $p_{i_1j_2}$ and the estimates of $p_{i_2i_2}$ and $p_{i_1i_1}$, which will be discussed in Chap. 4.

4. Estimation of Transition Rates in the Dichotomous Case

In the case where $s = 2$, it is possible to solve for the q_{ij}'s explicitly, given data from three observations, using either the internal cell frequencies or the marginal frequencies. The procedure is to use Eq. (2.4) or (2.7) to solve explicitly for the r_{ijt}'s in terms of the p_{i_t}'s or $p_{i_oj_t}$'s, and then to use Eq. (1.4) to solve for the q_{ij}'s in terms of the r_{ijt}'s. The states will be labelled 1 and 0, as will be our custom in notation for dichotomies.

First solving for r_{10t} and r_{01t}, using the marginal proportions only, Eq. (2.4) gives:

$$p_{1_1} = p_{1_0} r_{11\tau} + p_{0_0} r_{01\tau} \tag{4.1}$$

$$p_{1_2} = p_{1_1} r_{11t} + p_{0_1} r_{01t} \tag{4.2}$$

When the time periods τ (between observations 0 and 1) and t (between observations 1 and 2) are alike, and there is no evidence of exogenous disturbances to make the q_{ij} different at the two periods, we can assume that $r_{ij\tau} = r_{ijt}$ and solve for r_{ijt}. This gives

$$r_{01t} = \frac{p_{1_1}^2 - p_{1_0}p_{1_2}}{p_{1_1} - p_{1_0}} \tag{4.3}$$

$$r_{10t} = \frac{p_{1_0} + p_{1_2} - 2p_{1_1} + p_{1_1}^2 - p_{1_0}p_{1_2}}{p_{1_0} - p_{1_1}} \tag{4.4}$$

Equations (4.3) and (4.4) make evident the point that stable estimates can be obtained only under conditions far from statistical equilibrium, since only under such conditions will the denominator, $p_{1_1} - p_{1_0}$ not be a random variable, due principally to sampling variations in the response. Under most conditions, the estimates from internal cell frequencies are to be preferred. These are obtained by use of Eq. (2.7) as follows:

$$p_{1_01_2} = p_{1_01_1} r_{11t} + p_{1_00_1} r_{01t} \tag{4.5}$$

$$p_{0_01_2} = p_{0_01_1} r_{11t} + p_{0_00_1} r_{01t} \tag{4.6}$$

These equations may be solved for r_{01t} to give

$$r_{01t} = \frac{p_{1_01_1} p_{1_2} - p_{1_01_2} p_{1_1}}{p_{1_01_1} - p_{1_0} p_{1_1}} \tag{4.7}$$

and

$$r_{10t} = \frac{p_{1_01_1}(1 - p_{1_2}) - p_{1_01_2}(1 - p_{1_1}) + p_{1_0}(p_{1_2} - p_{1_1})}{p_{1_01_1} - p_{1_0} p_{1_1}} \tag{4.8}$$

This solution gives values for r_{01t} and r_{10t}, where t refers to the second time period, between observations 1 and 2. There is no need for the first time period τ to equal the second.

Having solved for the values of r_{01t} and r_{10t}, it is necessary to use Eq. (4.4) to obtain q_{01} and q_{10} as a function of r_{01t} and r_{10t}. The equation may be solved explicitly in the dichotomous case to give

$$q_{ij} = \frac{-r_{ijt}}{(r_{10t} + r_{01t})\,t} \, ln(1 - r_{10t} - r_{01t}) \tag{4.9}$$

This then provides the equations for estimating q_{ij} in the dichotomous case. The observed quantities n_{11}/n in the two tables cross tabulating times 0–1 and 0–2 are estimates of $p_{1_01_1}$ and $p_{1_01_2}$, and the observed quantities $n_{1.}/n$ and $n_{.1}/n$ are estimates of p_{1_0}, p_{1_1}, and p_{1_2}. These are used to estimate the values of r_{10t} and r_{01t}, by Eq. (4.7) and (4.8), and then Eq. (4.9) is used to estimate the values of q_{10} and q_{01}.

If it is desired to solve for the q_{ij} or for the sum of the transition rates, $q_{01} + q_{10}$, directly, Eq. (4.9) may be put in simpler form by use of Eqs. (4.7) and (4.8). First, the sum of the q_{ij}'s is given by:

$$q_{01} + q_{10} = \frac{1}{t} \, ln \frac{p_{1_01_1} - p_{1_0} p_{1_1}}{p_{1_01_2} - p_{1_0} p_{1_2}} \tag{4.10}$$

Then the value of q_{01} is given by

$$q_{01} = \frac{p_{1_01_1} p_{1_2} - p_{1_01_2} p_{1_1}}{(p_{1_01_1} - p_{1_01_2} + p_{1_0}(p_{1_2} - p_{1_1}))\,t} \, ln \frac{p_{1_01_1} - p_{1_0} p_{1_1}}{p_{1_01_2} - p_{1_0} p_{1_2}} \tag{4.11}$$

The equilibrium value of p_1 is given by $q_{01}/(q_{01} + q_{10})$, which is

$$p_{1_e} = \frac{p_{101_1} p_{1_2} - p_{101_2} p_{1_1}}{p_{101_1} - p_{101_2} + p_{10}(p_{1_2} - p_{1_1})} \tag{4.12}$$

It is useful to compare the estimates of individual change with those that derive from an ordinary Markov process involving no response uncertainty, as described in Chap. 1. This will be done in the case of various sets of real data in Chap. 3, but it will give an intuitive grasp of the difference to examine a simple, hypothetical case.

Suppose data were obtained at three points equally spaced in time, labelled 0, 1, and 2, which gave the cross tabulations shown in Table 2.1 (expressed in terms of proportions of the total sample).

Table 2.1

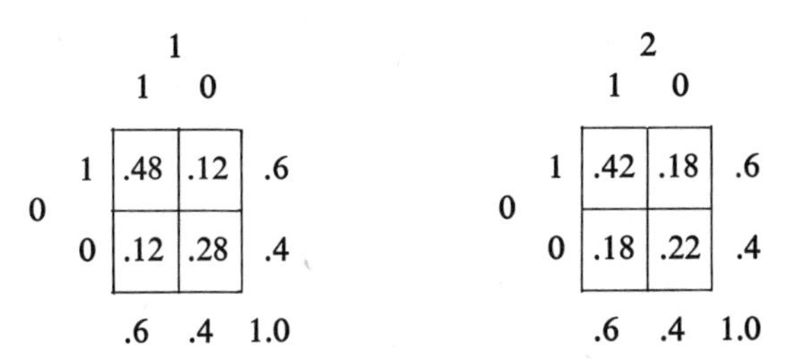

0 \ 1	1	0	
1	.48	.12	.6
0	.12	.28	.4
	.6	.4	1.0

0 \ 2	1	0	
1	.42	.18	.6
0	.18	.22	.4
	.6	.4	1.0

Such a pair of tables would have been produced (assuming no sampling fluctuations) by a simple two-state Markov process in which individuals were in either state 1 or 0, with no response uncertainty. If the process were continuous in time, the values of q'_{01} and q'_{10} that would have generated such data are 0.42 and 0.28, respectively.* If the process were a discrete time Markov chain, with periods coinciding with the observations, the values of the transition probabilities r'_{01} and r'_{10} that would have generated such data are 0.3 and 0.2, respectively. In either case, only one of the two cross tabulations is necessary in order to estimate the parameter values. The second cross tabulation, between times 0 and 2, would merely have confirmed the estimates made from the first, and would have indicated that in fact a straightforward Markov process with two states was operative.

Estimation of parameters for the model described in this chapter would use Eqs. (4.10) and (4.11) for q_{01} and q_{10}, and Eqs. (4.7) and (4.8) for r_{01t} and r_{10t}. Carrying out the calculations for q_{01} and q_{10} gives:

*The equation by which these values are obtained is

$$q_{ij} = \frac{-n_{ij}/n_{i.}}{(n_{ij}/n_{i.} + n_{ji}/n_{j.})t} \ln\left(1 - \frac{n_{ij}}{n_{i.}} - \frac{n_{ji}}{n_{j.}}\right)$$

For derivation of this equation, see Coleman (1964).

$$q_{01} = \frac{.48 \times .6 - .42 \times .6}{(.48 - .42 + 0)\,1}\, ln\, \frac{.48 - .6 \times .6}{.42 - .6 \times .6}$$

$$= .42$$

$$q_{10} = ln\, \frac{.48 - .6 \times .6}{.42 - .6 \times .6} = .42$$

$$= .28$$

Carrying out the calculations for r_{01t} and r_{10t} gives:

$$r_{01t} = \frac{.48 \times .6 - .42 \times .6}{.48 - .6 \times .6}$$

$$= 0.3$$

$$r_{10t} = \frac{.48 \times .4 - .42 \times .4}{.48 - .6 \times .6}$$

$$= 0.2$$

These values are identical to those estimated for the regular Markov process. However, since these parameters are transition rates and transition probabilities for the elements, it is necessary to translate them into expected amounts of change, Δv_{it}, for individuals at differing initial points v_1 between 0.0 and 1.0. The calculations carried out on page 25 for the case in which $r_{01t} = 0.3$ and $r_{10t} = 0.2$ may be used for this. They show that for individuals initially at $v_1 = 1.0$, the expected amount of change is -0.2; for those initially at $v_1 = 0.0$, the expected change is 0.3. Thus if all individuals were at one of these two points, the result is the same as for the regular Markov process, for there the expected proportion of individuals to move from state 0 to state 1 is 0.3. Thus the expected amount of change for any individual initially in state 0 is 0.3, and similarly for the value of 0.2 in the reverse direction.

This does not say, however, that the two models give the same results, for we do not know, in the latent Markov process, what proportion of individuals is at 1.0 and 0.0. This requires use of the knowledge that the time separating observations 0 and 1 equals that separating observations 1 and 2. With such knowledge, the analysis of Chap. 4 will show that, according to these data, all individuals are located at the extremes: .6 are at $v_1 = 1.0$, and .4 are at $v_1 = 0.0$. With this result, the model becomes identical to the simple two-state Markov process, and in this sense degenerates into the two-state process.

Let us consider a case, however, that does not fit the simple process. Suppose the data were, as in the empirical examples of Chap. 1, something like that in Table 2.2.

Table 2.2

		1: 1	1: 0	
0	1	.48	.12	.6
	0	.12	.28	.4
		.6	.4	1.0

		2: 1	2: 0	
0	1	.474	.126	.6
	0	.126	.274	.4
		.6	.4	1.0

In this case, the simple two-state Markov process would give estimates for q'_{01} and q'_{10} of 0.42 and 0.28, and for r'_{01} and r'_{10} of 0.3 and 0.2 from the 0–1 table, as before. However, these transition rates, or transition probabilities, would be incompatible with the 0–2 table. If instead the 0–2 table were used, the estimates of transition rates q'_{01} and q'_{10} would be 0.22 and 0.15, respectively, much smaller than those obtained from the 0–1 table. Treating the table as the outcome of a two-period Markov chain, as before, would give estimates of transition probabilities r'_{01} and r'_{10} of 0.19 and 0.12, respectively, equally incompatible with the estimates from the 0–1 table.

Using the latent Markov process, the estimates of transition rates are again obtained from application of Eqs. (4.10) and (4.11):

$$q_{01} = \frac{.48 \times .6 - .474 \times .6}{(.48 - .474 + 0)\,1} \, ln \, \frac{.48 - .6 \times .6}{.474 - .6 \times .6}$$

$$= 0.03$$

$$q_{10} = ln \, \frac{.48 - .6 \times .6}{.474 - .6 \times .6} - .03$$

$$= 0.02$$

The transition probabilities are obtained by application of Eqs. (4.7) and (4.8), as before:

$$r_{01t} = \frac{.48 \times .6 - .474 \times .6}{.48 - .6 \times .6}$$

$$= 0.03$$

$$r_{10t} = \frac{.48 \times .4 - .474 \times .4}{.48 - .6 \times .6}$$

$$= 0.02$$

In this case, the estimates of r_{ijt} and q_{ij} are alike, within the limits of rounding error. This will always be the case when $q_{ij}t$ is very small relative to 1.0. As $q_{ij}t$ approaches zero, the values of r_{ijt} for the Markov chain embedded within the process approach the values of $q_{ij}t$.

Since this process is at the level of the elements, it is necessary again to translate this into changes at the level of the individual, Δv_{1t}. Application of Eq. (3.1) shows that at $v_1 = 1$, the expected change is -0.02; at $v_1 = 0.5$, the expected change is $+0.005$; and at $v_1 = 0$, the expected change is $+0.03$. The methods of Chap. 4 will in turn show that in contrast to the preceding case, far from all individuals are at the extremes. In fact, the distribution is as if 0.36 of the sample were at $v_1 = 1$, 0.16 were at $v_1 = 0$, and 0.48 were at $v_1 = 0.5$. Thus the average amount of change for all individuals in the time period t between observations is even less than that indicated by the size of the transition probabilities. The average over all individuals of the absolute value of the expected change is only $.36 \times .03 + .48 \times .005 + .16 \times .02$, or .0164. In contrast, the simple two-state process would give as the average expected change in each period simply the observed change from the 0–1 table, $.12 + .12 = .24$. Using the calculations from the 0–2 table the change would be less, but not markedly so: $.6 \times .12 + .4 \times .19$, or .15.

The comparison between the results for the simple two-state Markov process and the latent process shows a sharp difference. The latent Markov process shows that almost no movement is occurring, and that most of the apparent change is merely response uncertainty. In this case, the estimates of change obtained by use of the simple two-state Markov process would have been extremely misleading, whether the 0–1 table or the 0–2 table were used for estimation.

In this simple example, the differences between the two-state Markov process and the latent process are wholly in the amounts of change; the relative sizes of the transition rates in the two directions are correctly estimated by the two-state process. This will always be so when the system is in aggregate equilibrium, as in this example; but in various other cases, when the system is not at equilibrium, even the relative values of q_{ij} or r_{ijt} will be in error by use of the simple model.

5. Measurement of Causal Relations in the Case of Multiple Stimuli

Before turning to the empirical data to be analyzed, there is one other task to be accomplished. This is the examination of causal relations among attributes. Until now, we have treated a multistate model as merely multiple responses to a single stimulus. But suppose we consider simultaneously the response to two or more stimuli. If the possible responses on each are dichotomous, then the total number of states of the individual is $2 \times 2 = 4$ for two stimuli, or 2^w for w stimuli.

When we study changes of two or more such attributes in conjunction, the principal interest ordinarily is in causation—effects of being in a given state on one attribute on the q_{ij} for changes in one state on another.

This process, then, we will postulate at the level of the elements, proposing that an element may be conditioned to more than one stimulus at the same time, and that if an element is conditioned to state 1 on attribute X_1, this may add to its transition rate toward a given state on attribute X_2. This means that in a system of responses to multiple stimuli, the sizes of the transition rates q_{ij} between states may be studied for those effects of attributes on one another.

We will treat here the case of additive, or otherwise simple, effects on q_{ij}, rather than more complex effects. Just as in the case of continuous variables, it is likely that such a model will have a wide range of applicability.

There are two possible directions of effect of other attributes or variables on an attribute composed of two discrete classes. One is an effect toward producing shifts of an element from state 1 to state 0, that is, an effect in increasing q_{10}. The other is an effect toward producing shifts from state 0 to state 1, that is, an effect in increasing q_{01}. The transition rate q_{10} may thus be seen to be made up of components, each component representing the effect of these other states toward state 0 of X_1. For concreteness, we consider a case in which the element is characterized by one other stimulus with a dichotomous response, attribute X_2. The element is thus characterized simultaneously by state 1 or 0 of the dependent attribute X_1 and state 1 or 0 of the independent attribute X_2. Using the right-hand position for X_1 and the second position for X_2, the four states of the element are 11, 10, 01, 00, with change in X_1 being between states 11 and 10 and states 01 and 00. Notation used in subscripts for q_{ij} in the study of multiple stimuli will treat these state labels as binary numbers and utilize their decimal representation, 3, 2, 1, 0. Thus the transition rates between states 11 and 10 are q_{32} and q_{23}, and the transition rates between state 01 and 00 are q_{10} and q_{01}. A graph showing the configuration of states and movements of elements between them is shown in Fig. 2.1.

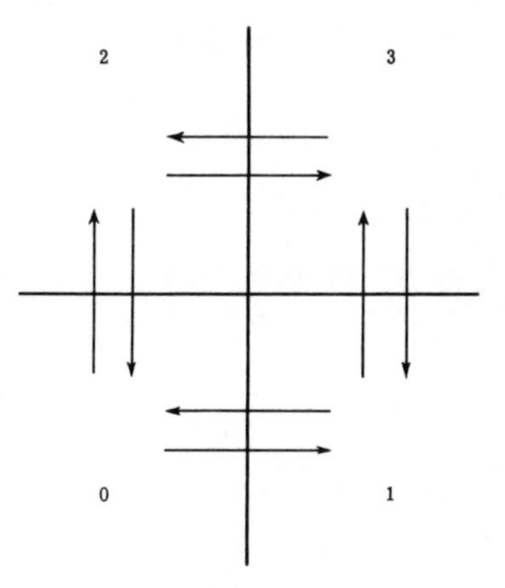

Figure 2.1.

For a larger number of independent attributes, the transition rates are labelled similarly. Thus for attributes X_2 and X_3 as independent variables, one shift is from 110 to 111, and the transition rate is labelled q_{67}. Considering the effects of attributes X_2 and X_3 in shifting from state 0 of X_1 to state 1 of X_1, this transition rate would be partitioned as follows:

$$q_{67} = \alpha_{31} + \alpha_{21} + \alpha_{.1} \tag{5.1}$$

where α_{k1} is the effect of state 1 of attribute X_k in shifting X_1 from 0 to 1, and $\alpha_{.1}$ is a random component representing the effect of all unknown attributes in shifting X_1 from 0 to 1. Using α'_{k1} to indicate the effect of state 0 of X_k on shifting the element from 0 to 1 on X_1, the other transition rates in this direction are:

$$\begin{aligned} q_{45} &= \alpha_{31} + \alpha'_{21} + \alpha_{.1} \\ q_{23} &= \alpha'_{31} + \alpha_{21} + \alpha_{.1} \\ q_{01} &= \alpha'_{31} + \alpha'_{21} + \alpha_{.1} \end{aligned}$$

Using β_{k1} and β'_{k1} to indicate the effect of states 1 and 0 of attribute X_k in shifting X_1 in the opposite direction, from 1 to 0, the transition rates are:

$$\begin{aligned} q_{76} &= \beta_{31} + \beta_{21} + \beta_{.1} \\ q_{54} &= \beta_{31} + \beta'_{21} + \beta_{.1} \\ q_{32} &= \beta'_{31} + \beta_{21} + \beta_{.1} \\ q_{10} &= \beta'_{31} + \beta'_{21} + \beta_{.1} \end{aligned} \tag{5.2}$$

Since states 1 and 0 of each independent attribute are exhaustive, it is never possible to isolate the separate effects α_{k1} and α'_{k1}. But it is possible to assess the differential effects of the two states, for if we define

$$a_{k1} = \alpha_{k1} - \alpha'_{k1} \tag{5.3}$$

and

$$a_{.1} = \sum \alpha'_{k1} + \alpha_{.1} \tag{5.4}$$

then

$$\begin{aligned} q_{67} &= a_{31} + a_{21} + a_{.1} \\ q_{45} &= a_{31} \phantom{+ a_{21}} + a_{.1} \\ q_{23} &= \phantom{a_{31} +} a_{21} + a_{.1} \\ q_{01} &= \phantom{a_{31} + a_{21}} + a_{.1} \end{aligned} \tag{5.5}$$

With similar definitions for b_{k1} and $b_{.1}$, the transition rates for moving X_1 from state 1 to state 0 become

$$\begin{aligned} q_{76} &= b_{31} + b_{21} + b_{.1} \\ q_{54} &= b_{31} \phantom{+ b_{21}} + b_{.1} \\ q_{32} &= \phantom{b_{31} +} b_{21} + b_{.1} \\ q_{10} &= \phantom{b_{31} + b_{21}} + b_{.1} \end{aligned} \tag{5.6}$$

Thus in the case of two independent attributes, a_{21} and a_{31} can be obtained as an average of two differences:

$$a_{31} = \tfrac{1}{2}(q_{67} - q_{23} + q_{45} - q_{01})$$
$$a_{21} = \tfrac{1}{2}(q_{67} - q_{45} + q_{23} - q_{01}) \tag{5.7}$$

The quantity $a_{.1}$ is obtained from Eq. (5.5):

$$a_{.1} = \tfrac{1}{4}((q_{67} - a_{31} - a_{21}) + (q_{45} - a_{31}) + (q_{23} - a_{21}) + q_{01}) \tag{5.8}$$

Substituting from Eq. (5.7) for a_{31} and a_{21} gives $a_{.1}$ in terms of q_{ij}:

$$a_{.1} = \tfrac{1}{4}(3q_{01} + q_{23} + q_{45} - q_{67}) \tag{5.9}$$

Similar equations for b_{31}, b_{21}, and $b_{.1}$ may be obtained from Eq. (5.6).

If a_{k1} is positive, α_{k1} is greater than α'_{k1}, and there is a net effect of state 1 of X_k on the change in X_1 from state 0 to state 1. If a_{k1} is negative, α'_{k1} is greater than α_{k1}, and there is a net effect of state 0 of X_k. The negative sign on a_{k1} merely indicates that the net effect of X_k is from state 0. Consequently, the value of $a_{.1}$ includes both the residual change in X_1 and the components a_{k1} that are negative. The residual change, a_{r1}, is obtained from $a_{.1}$ by subtracting the absolute values of all a_{k1} that are negative:

$$a_{r1} = a_{.1} + \sum a_{k1} \tag{5.10}$$

where the summation is taken only over those values of a_{k1} that are negative.

In the general case of w independent attributes, the effects of attribute k on attribute h are given by an average of differences taken over all pairs of q_{ij} that differ only by a_{kh}. There are 2^{w-1} such pairs, and the equation is

$$a_{kh} = \frac{1}{2^{w-1}} \sum (q_{ij} - q_{i'j'}) \tag{5.11}$$

The quantity $a_{.h}$ is obtained as the average of all q_{ij}'s from state 0 to state 1 reduced by the components a_{kh} that enter into each q_{ij}:

$$a_{.h} = \frac{1}{2^{w}} \sum (q_{ij} - A_{ij}) \tag{5.12}$$

where A_{ij} is the sum of those a_{kh} that enter into q_{ij}.

The subscripts on q_{ij} can provide aid in determining which q_{ij}'s represent change of particular types. Thus in Eq. (5.11) the relation between k, h, ij and $i'j'$ are:

(a) the differences $j - i$ and $j' - i'$ are each equal to 2^{h-1}

(b) the differences $i - i'$ and $j - j'$ are each equal to 2^{k-1}

Similar relations hold for b_{kh}, except that the differences $j - i$ and $j' - i'$ are equal to $- 2^{h-1}$.

In Eq. (5.12) for $a_{.h}$, if A_{ij} is expressed, as in Eq. (5.9), in terms of the q_{ij}'s from which the a_{kh}'s were obtained, then the sum of the subscripts (giving the subscript the same sign as its parent q) are:

$$\frac{1}{2^{w-1}} \sum i = 0$$

$$\frac{1}{2^{w-1}} \sum j = 2^{h-1}$$

For example, in Eq. (5.9):

$$\tfrac{1}{2}(0 + 2 + 4 - 6) = 0, \text{ and } \tfrac{1}{2}(1 + 3 + 5 - 7) = 1.$$

For $b_{.h}$, the roles of i and j are reversed.

For many situations, such a study of causal relations is not applicable, for only a sequence of responses to a single stimulus is under study. Some of the data to be analyzed in the next chapter are of that sort. However, for the case where simultaneous change in response to two or more stimuli is under study, the focus on causation becomes possible. For such cases, then, the results of the preceding section are necessary to answer the question of what states of what attributes are affecting others. Because of the complexity of such a situation, we have developed a model of causation only for the case of dichotomous attributes.

6. Calculation of q_{ij} from r_{ijt}

Given estimates of the values of r_{ijt} obtained as indicated in Sec. 2, estimates of the values of q_{ij} may be obtained by use of Eq. (1.4). Considering only those values of r_{ijt} for which $i \neq j$ (and thus $\delta_{ij} = 0$), and for which $q_{ij} \neq 0$, transposition may be carried out on Eq. (1.4) to give the following equation for a system of s states:

$$q_{ij} = r_{ijt} - \frac{t^2}{2} \sum_{k=1}^{s} q_{ik} q_{kj} - \frac{t^3}{3!} \sum_{k=1}^{s} \sum_{h=1}^{s} q_{ik} q_{kh} q_{hj} - \cdots \tag{6.1}$$

This equation may be used in an iterative procedure, using the observed data for the estimate of r_{ijt}, and values $q_{ij}^{(m)}$ on the right-hand side obtained in the m-th iteration to calculate values $q_{ij}^{(m+1)}$ for the $m + 1$ iteration. The values $q_{ij}^{(0)}$ may be taken to be zero, so that the estimate for $q_{ij}^{(1)}$ is r_{ijt}. The series is extended on each iteration until the last calculated term is less than some threshold of accuracy; and the iteration proceeds until each q_{ij} on the $m + 1$ iteration differs from the corresponding q_{ij} on the m-th iteration by less than some criterion of desired accuracy. In some cases, when the data are not compatible with the model, it is necessary to obtain approximate values of q_{ij} by arbitrarily truncating the series after a few terms.

It is also possible to estimate the q_{ij}'s by hand, through a simpler, but somewhat less flexible, procedure. If the matrix of transition probabilities r_{ijt} is labelled R, it is obvious from consideration of Eq. (1.3) to (1.6) that

$$R = e^{Qt} \tag{6.2}$$

Taking the logarithm of both sides gives

$$ln\ R = Qt$$

The logarithm of the matrix R is defined as the expansion of $R - I$ in a power series.

$$ln\ R = R - I - \frac{(R-I)^2}{2} + \frac{(R-I)^3}{3} - + \ldots \tag{6.3}$$

If this expansion is carried out until the next term is smaller than an arbitrary threshold, and then corresponding terms in the successive matrices are summed, the result will be an estimate of Qt.* (The elements of Qt are $q_{ij}t$.)

The advantage of this method is that it may be carried out much more easily by hand than the procedure described previously. The advantage of the previously described iterative procedure is that one may arbitrarily fix certain q_{ij}'s to 0 or to some other value, and then solve for the remaining q_{ij}'s, subject to this constraint. The usefulness of this device is evident in Sec. 5, where on theoretical grounds we introduced constraints, setting some q_{ij}'s to zero.

A computer program written in Fortran for the IBM 7090, which will carry out this iteration, is included in the appendix.

* I am indebted to M. Tainiter for making me aware of this method of estimating Q. See Tainiter (1962), who has also proved that the sum in (6.3) converges whenever $r_{iit} > 1/2$.

CHAPTER THREE

Empirical Examination of Change in the Presence of Response Uncertainty

Using the methods of the preceding chapter, it is possible to examine change when it occurs in data that also show response uncertainty. The present chapter will be devoted to several such sets of data drawn from diverse situations.

The data necessary to carry out such study are as indicated in Chap. 1: three or more responses to the same stimulus by a sample of individuals, a long sequence of responses to the same stimulus by a single individual, or some combination of these.

1. Distortion of Judgment Under Group Pressure

Solomon Asch (1951) carried out a series of experiments that strikingly demonstrated the effect of group pressures in modifying the judgment of an individual subject to these pressures. The individual was asked to compare the length of a line to the lengths of three other lines by indicating which of the other three was the same length. He was asked after three or more other persons (in various experimental conditions) had given their judgments. When *their* judgments were incorrect (in collusion with the experimenter), many subjects also gave incorrect judgments, succumbing to the pressure to give a judgment that would be correct in the eyes of other persons.

Bernard Cohen (1962), following Asch's general procedure, carried out experiments to study the process through which this distortion occurred. Cohen used groups of six persons plus the naïve subject over a sequence of thirty-six trials. By thus studying the responses through time, Cohen could study changes, and thus infer the process by which the changes came about. One person's responses, for example, were as follows for the thirty-six trials (where 1 equals objectively correct response, and 0 equals objectively incorrect response in conformity to the group): 101101011010101111101000010101110100.

Cohen studied two experimental conditions. In the "moderate" condition, the difference between the correct and incorrect lines was small (though large enough not to cause error in judgment when individuals were alone). Thirty-three subjects were tested in this experimental condition. In the "extreme" condition, the difference between the correct and incorrect lines was greater. Twenty-seven subjects were tested in this condition. In both conditions, there was extreme variation among subjects, some never giving an incorrect judgment, and others almost never giving a correct one.

Cohen used a model derived from the Bush-Mosteller learning model. He assumed that individuals could be in one of four states. These states were conceived as being along a line, in the sense that movement could occur only between states 1 and 2, 2 and 3, and 3 and 4. When in states 1 and 2, he gave a correct response; when in states 3 and 4, an incorrect one. The difference between the end states (1, 4) and the intermediate ones (2, 3) was that the end states were absorbing states, while the intermediate ones were transient. Thus once in an end state, the individual would never again move out and would henceforth always give a correct response (if in state 1) or an incorrect one (if in state 4). Cohen's model is a discrete-time Markov process in which the state corresponds directly to the response.

Without making a direct comparison of the model of this monograph with that of Cohen, I will apply the present model to Cohen's data. Cohen has carried out extensive tests of the fit of various forms of his model, and such analysis would go beyond the space that we can devote to his data. Thus Cohen's data will be used to illustrate this model's applicability; the model is not used for an exhaustive analysis of the data.

The behavior of these individuals makes these data appear particularly appropriate here—for they showed great differences in their response to group pressure. The over-all distribution of subjects in the proportion of incorrect judgments they made shows this. As Figs. 3.1 and 3.2 show, nearly all individuals were near one of the extremes. Of course such an aggregation over the thirty-six responses disregards changes they may have made; but it is evident from these figures that, along with whatever changes might have occurred, there was a great deal of variability among the subjects.

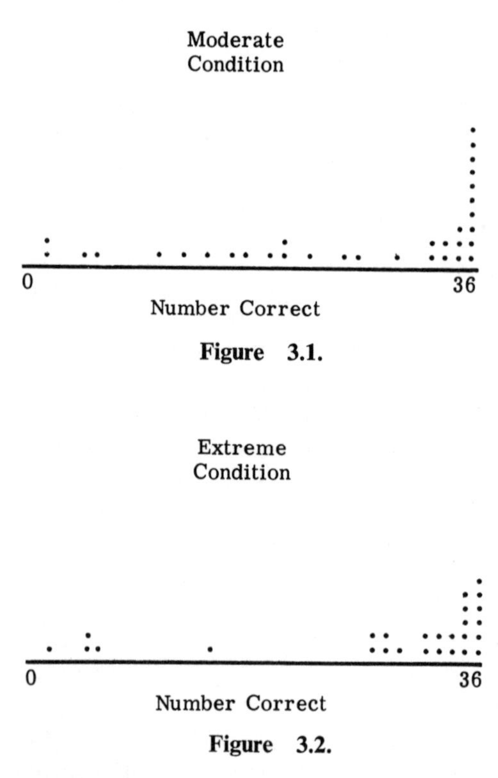

Figure 3.1.

Figure 3.2.

It is in such a situation that a simple Markov process, which aggregates over individuals and treats the resulting proportion as a probability for each, would be highly inappropriate and would not fit the data.*

The question that can reasonably be asked, then, is: Is there change, and if so, how much? It is evident that there is variability among individuals; but that will be studied in Chap. 5. The present question concerns change.

There are two possible ways of aggregating these data to study the question—across time for one individual and across individuals. Aggregation across time for a single individual allows separate estimates of the rates of movement for different individuals; aggregation across individuals for a given time allows separate estimates for each trial in the experiment. However, such aggregation does not provide enough data to permit stable estimates for single individuals or single trials. There are only thirty-three and twenty-seven individuals in the two experiments, and each individual's sequence is only thirty-six responses long. In addition, the relatively large number of persons who never deviated or who deviated only once or twice from the correct response makes the effective number of persons even less.

Taking the subject whose responses are reproduced above and aggregating over the trials gives Table 3.1, which shows the kinds of tables that would exist if aggregation over time were carried out.

These tables are quite erratic. Comparison of t vs. $t + 1$ and t vs. $t + 2$ shows behavior that is the reverse of change—as if alternation were occurring. But comparison of t vs. $t + 2$ and t vs. $t + 3$ shows behavior that suggests change—a decline in the main diagonal cells.

* About the best that one could do with such a model would be to divide the subjects into two groups—those who made many incorrect judgments and those who made few—and to use two Markov processes. Such a procedure can be viewed as an approximation to the present one, which allows individuals to be at any point on the continuum between 0.0 and 1.0 in their probability of giving a correct response.

Table 3.1. Cross tabulation between adjacent trials, those at one remove and those at two, for a single individual.

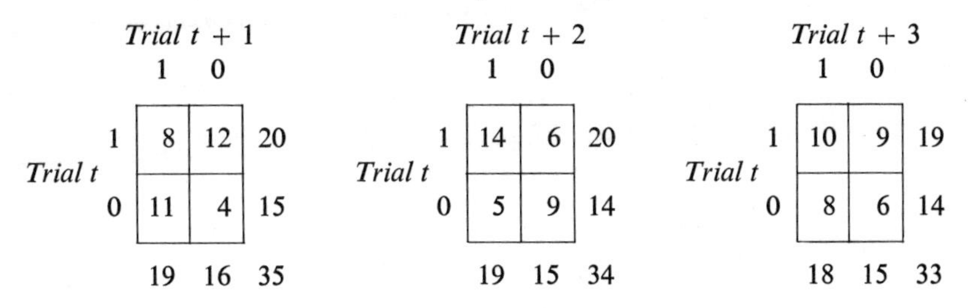

Trial t	Trial $t+1$: 1	0	Total
1	8	12	20
0	11	4	15
Total	19	16	35

Trial t	Trial $t+2$: 1	0	Total
1	14	6	20
0	5	9	14
Total	19	15	34

Trial t	Trial $t+3$: 1	0	Total
1	10	9	19
0	8	6	14
Total	18	15	33

Because the data are too sparse for aggregating in either of these single ways, aggregation both over individuals and over time are necessary.

Equation (4.10) of Chap. 2 is used to obtain estimates of the total change, $q_{01} + q_{10}$ (which will be called k). Considering all adjacent pairs of trials as the 0–1 table, and those separated by one trial as the 0–2 table, the tabulations resulting from these data are as shown in Table 3.2.

Table 3.2. Cross tabulation between adjacent trials and trials at one remove for Cohen's data.

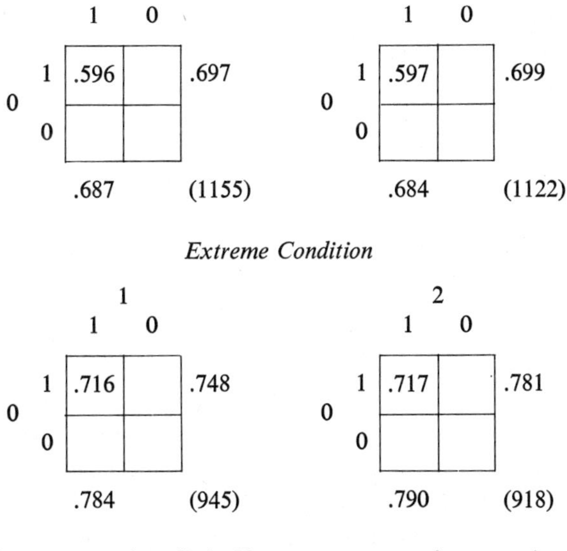

Moderate Condition

0	1: 1	0	
1	.596		.697
0			
	.687		(1155)

0	2: 1	0	
1	.597		.699
0			
	.684		(1122)

Extreme Condition

0	1: 1	0	
1	.716		.748
0			
	.784		(945)

0	2: 1	0	
1	.717		.781
0			
	.790		(918)

These tables suggest that little if any movement is occurring. There is a slight *increase* in the main diagonal, though only in the moderate condition does this result in the value of $p_{1_0 1_2} - p_{1_0} p_{1_2}$ being slightly larger than $p_{1_0 1_1} - p_{1_0} p_{1_1}$. As a consequence, the moderate condition gives a value of

$q_{01} + q_{10}$ that is negative, incompatible with the model of regular change.

However, the matter can be tested further by use of pairs of responses further separated in time. It could well be that the data above show merely chance variations.

To use pairs of responses further separated in time requires a slight modification of Eq. (4.10) of Chap. 2. If t is taken to be the separation between two trials (for adjacent trials $t = 1$), then an equation like (4.10) can be derived using p_{1010}:

$$q_{01} + q_{10} = k = \frac{1}{t} \ln \frac{p_{1010} - p_{10}^2}{p_{101t} - p_{10}p_{1t}}$$

This can be put in slightly different form:

$$kt = \ln(p_{1010} - p_{10}^2) - \ln(p_{101t} - p_{10}p_{1t})$$

Now for various values of t, $\ln(p_{101t} - p_{10}p_{1t})$ can be estimated from the data. The value of k can be estimated from the slope of the resulting line, and the value of p_{1010} at the intercept of $t = 0$, since the equation is in the form of $bx = a + y$, where $x = t$, $b = k$, and $y = -\ln(p_{101t} - p_{10}p_{1t})$. At the same time, the model can be tested by the linearity of the plot. If the data show linearity with a positive slope, then they indicate that regular movement is occurring, as hypothesized by the model.

Figure 3.3 shows the plot of $-\ln(p_{101t} - p_{10}p_{1t})$ vs. t. (The Fortran computer program for tabulating these responses and carrying out calculations is included in the appendix.)

The extreme condition shows a slope that appears to be quite linear except for the estimates based on $t = 30 - 35$, where the number of cases is small anyway. The value of the slope is .0114. The moderate condition shows a slope that is much less linear, diminishing to near zero for small values of t and rising sharply for large values of t. The increase in slope with increasing t seems considerably more than could be due to small numbers of cases in the estimate. It appears clear that the more widely separated the trials used in estimating k, the higher the estimated value of k. Taking the values of the slope at the portion of the line that is nearly linear, the approximate value of k is .0050.

In both cases, the slope, or the total rate of movement, is very small. Most of the apparent changes are mere manifestations of an underlying response probability that is relatively stable.

The rising slope for very widely spaced observations not only is inconsistent with the model, but also suggests other behavior: as if there were sharp changes that occurred either close to the beginning or close to the end of the experiment. To examine this possibility further, the experiment was divided in half, with the first eighteen responses and the second eighteen

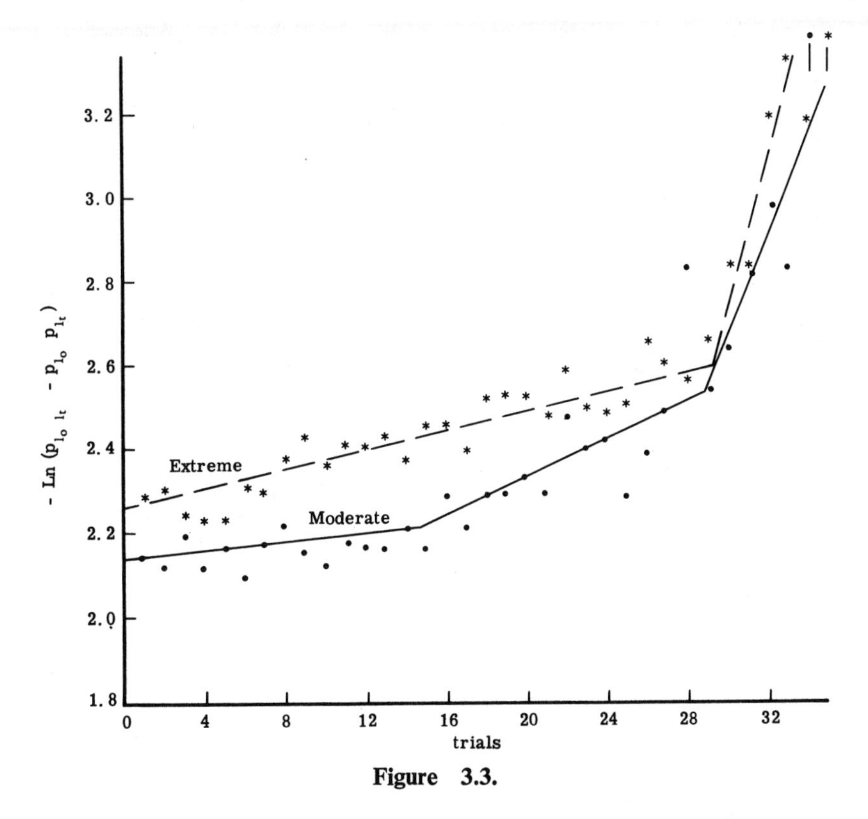

Figure 3.3.

considered separately. The results of these calculations are shown in Figs. 3.4 and 3.5. As the zero or near-zero slope of Fig. 3.5 shows, the last eighteen responses indicate that there is no change or very slight change over the whole of this period. The difference in intercepts shows that the values of $p_{1o1o} - p_{1o}p_{1o}$ were quite different for the two conditions, but this has to do with differences in response uncertainty in the two cases, and its examination will be reserved until Chap. 5.

The first eighteen responses, in contrast, show the same increase in slope that the total experiment showed. The lack of a straight slope again suggests that there was differential movement at different times, presumably greater movement at the beginning. Consequently, the first twelve responses were taken separately in an attempt to see whether, during this period, the movement appeared to be regular.

Figure 3.6 shows clearly that the slopes are high in this period. In the moderate condition, the slope is particularly high on the last six points, and still appears to show the tendency to increase. In the extreme condition, the slope appears to be more linear, suggesting that change occurred throughout this early period.

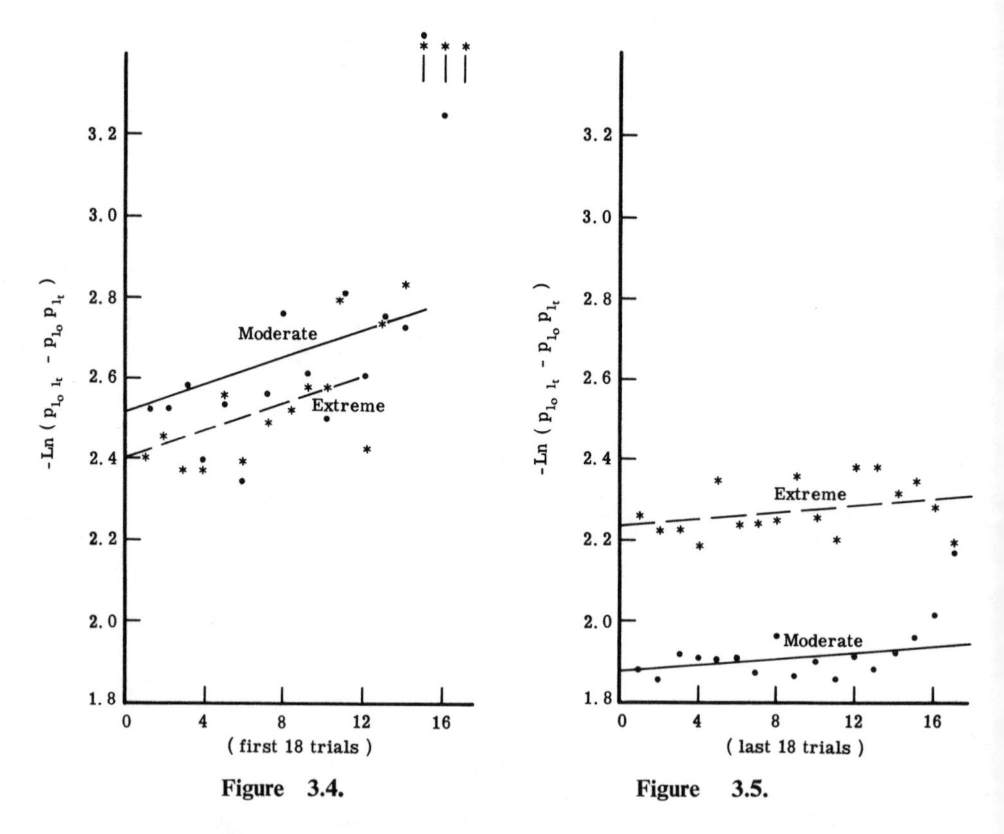

Figure 3.4. **Figure 3.5.**

It is difficult to tell more than this from these data. If there were more subjects, it would be possible to examine the change at each trial. There is a suggestion in the moderate condition that change occurred rather sharply around the sixth trial in those for whom change occurred at all, and that there was little or no change beyond that point. In the extreme condition, the data behave as if change were rather regular in the first twelve trials, but after that point (or at least after eighteen trials) no more change occurred.

2. Interdependence of Two Attributes

Another application of this model is to the study of the structure of relations between two or more attributes. For example, one study (McDill and Coleman, 1963) used questionnaire responses from the fall of the freshman year and the spring of the senior year in high school to infer the interdependences between plans to attend college, membership in the school's leading crowd, and interest in scholastic achievement. A major difficulty in

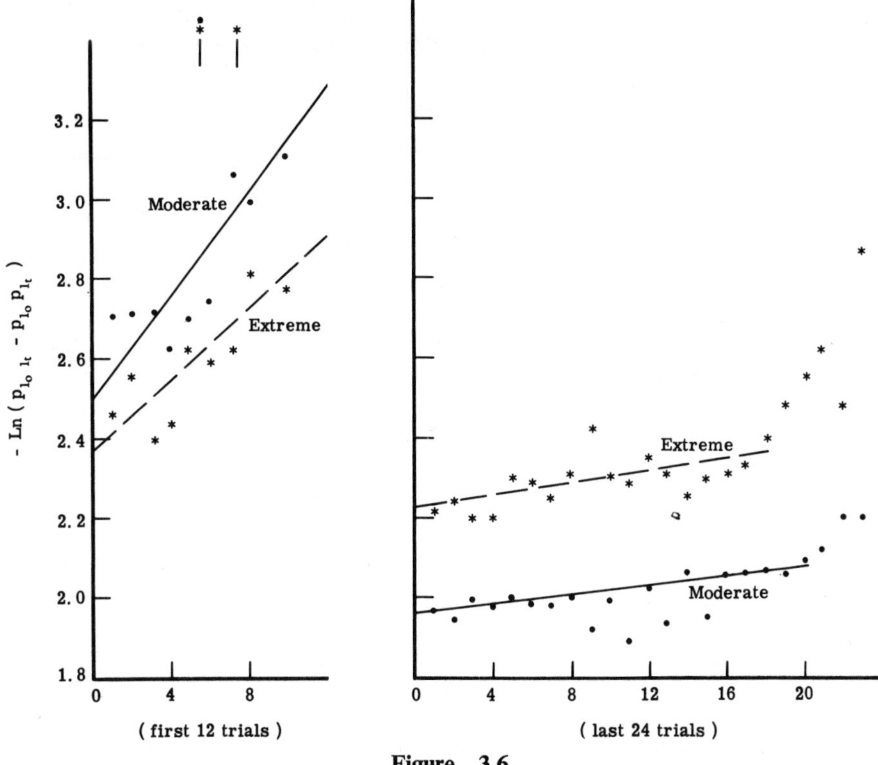

Figure 3.6.

all such analyses is the possibility that response unreliability produces the apparent change and thus gives spurious effects. Such response unreliability can be ferretted out with a three-wave panel, using the methods presented in Chap. 2.

From this study, tabulations were made of college plans vs. membership in the leading crowd, for fall vs. spring of the freshman year, and for fall of the freshman year vs. spring of the senior year.* These tabulations are shown in Table 3.3.

The problem that can be studied with these data is the effect of college plans on membership in the leading crowd and vice versa. At all three points in time, the two attributes are positively related, suggesting the possibility that either or both affect the other in a positive direction.

* The data are not exactly comparable to the McDill-Coleman data, for the measure of membership in the leading crowd is self-reported here, while in that paper it was based on nominations from others. A measure of membership in the leading crowd based on nominations from others was not constructed for the spring of the freshman year, and thus this measure could not be used in the present analysis.

Table 3.3. College plans and membership in the leading crowd of high school students. Attribute 1: college plans (1 = yes; 0 = no or undecided); attribute 2: self-perceived membership in leading crowd (1 = yes; 0 = no).

Spring Freshman

			3	2	1	0	
		2	1	1	0	0	
		1	1	0	1	0	*Total*
	3	1 1	87	21	14	3	125
Fall	2	1 0	6	60	1	29	96
Freshman	1	0 1	24	8	93	24	149
	0	0 0	11	38	14	128	191
		Total	128	127	122	184	561

Spring Senior

			3	2	1	0	
		2	1	1	0	0	
		1	1	0	1	0	*Total*
	3	1 1	75	24	12	14	125
Fall	2	1 0	17	46	2	31	96
Freshman	1	0 1	44	16	58	31	149
	0	0 0	17	49	25	100	191
		Total	153	135	97	176	561

The model that will be used for such study of these two attributes is that indicated in Chap. 2, where movement may proceed along any path indicated in Fig. 3.7. In an analysis that did not take into account response unreliability, we would assume each individual to be in one of the four indicated states at any time, with his response at that time identical to the state he is in. In contrast, with the model under study in this book, it is the *elements* that move from one of these four states to another, and the individual may at any time be in some intermediate state, depending on the state of his response elements.

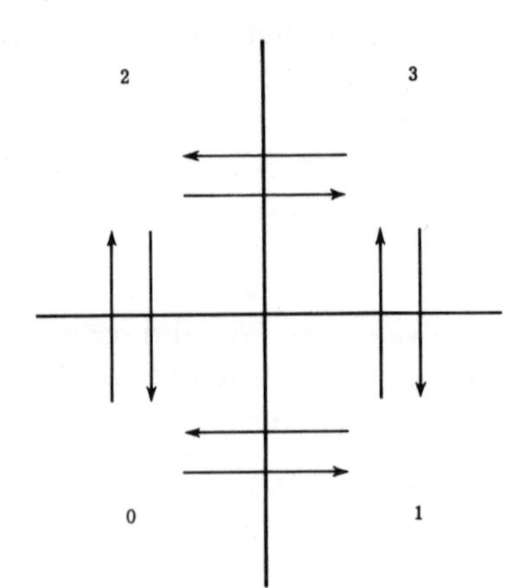

Figure 3.7.

Thus for comparison with the results of the analysis, it will be useful to carry out an analysis with both pairs of two-wave cross tabulations, assuming no response unreliability. Such an analysis leads to estimates of the transition rates, and thence to measures of effect, as shown in Table 3.4.*

Table 3.4. Transition rates and measures of effect for college plans vs. membership in the leading crowd, assuming no response uncertainty and homogeneous transition rates. College plans = attribute 1; leading crowd = attribute 2.

	Freshman fall—freshman spring q_{ij}		*Freshman fall—senior spring* q_{ij}	
$q_{23} = \alpha_{21} + \alpha_{.1}$	.376	$a'_{21} = .052,\ a'_{.1} = .376$	.329	$a_{21} = .047,\ a_{.1} = .282$
$q_{01} = \alpha'_{21} + \alpha_{.1}$	.428		.282	
$q_{32} = \beta_{21} + \beta_{.1}$	1.020	$b_{21} = .088,\ b_{.1} = .932$	.367	$b'_{21} = .067,\ b'_{.1} = .367$
$q_{10} = \beta'_{21} + \beta_{.1}$	.932		.434	
$q_{13} = \alpha_{12} + \alpha_{.2}$	.964	$a'_{12} = .244,\ a'_{.2} = .964$	.578	$a_{12} = .021,\ a_{.2} = .557$
$q_{02} = \alpha'_{12} + \alpha_{.2}$	1.208		.557	
$q_{31} = \beta_{12} + \beta_{.2}$	.664	$b'_{12} = 1.172,\ b'_{.2} = .664$	.182	$b'_{12} = .526,\ b'_{.2} = .182$
$q_{20} = \beta'_{12} + \beta_{.2}$	1.836		.708	

The measures of effect in Table 3.4 show several points of interest. First, the 0–1 table shows effects of lack of membership in the leading crowd toward forming college plans ($a'_{21} = .052$), membership in the leading crowd toward abandoning college plans ($b_{21} = .088$), lack of college plans toward gaining membership in the leading crowd ($a'_{12} = .244$), and lack of college plans strongly toward losing membership in the leading crowd ($b'_{12} = 1.172$). The effects, except for the last, b'_{12}, are much smaller than the random shocks.

These results are rather difficult to interpret: membership in the leading crowd apparently leads one to drop college plans if they exist, and inhibits their formation if they do not exist. Those without college plans are more likely to gain entrance into the leading crowds, but they are also more likely to be dropped from the crowd.

Comparing this with the results of the 0–2 table shows very different results through the four years in school. All effects except the last are reversed. In accordance with the McDill–Coleman paper, these results indicate that membership in the leading crowd leads to both formation and maintenance of college plans, and that college plans lead to both gaining and holding membership in the leading crowd.

Because of the greater time span, we would ordinarily place greater confidence in the freshman-senior changes. The apparent changes during the

* The time period freshman fall to senior spring is treated as four times the time period from freshman fall to freshman spring. The longer period is taken as $t = 1$, and thus the time period for the shorter is $t = 1/4$. Since the numerical method for solving for the q_{ij}'s arbitrarily takes t as 1, the transition rates from time 0–1 were multiplied by 4 to standardize all rates to the same time period.

freshman year, for example, may have been principally response unreliability. This conjecture is reinforced by the fact that when standardized to the same time unit, all rates are much higher for this early period than for the four-year period. If most of the apparent change over the freshman year was unreliability, and if a slow regular change was in progress over the four years, then we would expect the apparent freshman-year rates to be higher. If we label the apparent rates q_{ij}, the actual rates q^*_{ij}, and the unreliability component u_{ij}, then

$$\text{0–1 estimates: } q_{ij} = 4\left(u_{ij} + \frac{t}{4} q^*_{ij}\right)$$

$$\text{0–2 estimates: } q_{ij} = u_{ij} + t q^*_{ij}$$

Thus if the actual change were regular over the four years, then the 0–1 estimates would have an unreliability component four times as large as the 0–2 estimates.

An idea of the size of the unreliability component compared to the transition rates q^*_{ij} can be obtained by using the above equations applied to the sum of all the transition rates. (These equations, of course, are *ad hoc*, and intended only for rough comparisons, since there is no rationale to suggest that unreliability and actual rates of change combine additively to produce the observed q_{ij}'s.) The sum of the a_{ij}'s, b_{ij}'s, and random shocks for the 0–1 period (standardized to four-year time units) may be found, from Table 3.4, to be 4.490. The sum for the 0–2 period is found to be 2.049. Using the above equations

$$4u + q^* = 4.490$$
$$u + q^* = 2.049$$

Therefore, $3u = 2.441$, or $u = .813$. Consequently, $q^* = 2.049 - .813$, or $q^* = 1.236$. This gives a rough idea of the relative magnitude of the actual change and unreliability components in the observed transition rates.*

* An idea of the unreliability and change for each of the transition rates can be obtained by use of the above equations for each rate separately. Doing this gives:

u_{ij}	q^*_{ij}		
.016	.313	$a_{21} = .078$	$a_{.1} = .235$
.047	.235		
.218	.149	$b'_{21} = .119$	$b'_{.1} = .149$
.166	.268		
.129	.449	$a_{12} = .109$	$a_{.1} = .340$
.217	.340		
.161	.021	$b'_{12} = .311$	$b'_{.2} = .021$
.376	.332		

These are somewhat more in line with the estimates to be found from the unreliability-change model than are either of the two-wave estimates, though there are still great differences.

By use of the computer program contained in the appendix, the data in Table 3.3 were used to solve for the values of r_{ijt} (where t is the three years from freshman spring to senior spring). These were then used to estimate the values of q_{ij}. These values, together with the estimates of effect and random shock derived from the q_{ij}'s, are given in Table 3.5.

Table 3.5. Estimates of transition probabilities from data of Table 3.3, estimates of transition rates obtained from transition probabilities, and estimates of effects and random shocks. (Effects and random shocks are multiplied by 4/3 for comparability with Table 3.4.)

	Values of r_{ijt}					*Values of* q_{ij}			
	3	2	1	0		3	2	1	0
3	.769	.100	.052	.079	3		.140	.072	0
2	.215	.074	−.050	.162	2	.299		0	.256
1	.263	.045	.578	.115	1	.368	0		.180
0	−.026	.169	.143	.714	0	0	.267	.225	

Measures of effect and random shocks (multiplied by 4/3 so that the unit of time is the total four years of school).

$a_{21} = .100$	$a_{.1} = .300$	*forming college plans*
$b'_{21} = .053$	$b'_{.1} = .240$	*abandoning college plans*
$a_{12} = .135$	$a_{.2} = .356$	*gaining membership in crowd*
$b'_{12} = .053$	$b'_{.2} = .187$	*losing membership in crowd*

These estimates of effect show that membership in the crowd led to forming college plans ($a_{21} = .100$), lack of membership led to abandoning them ($b'_{21} = .053$), the existence of college plans led to gaining membership in the crowd ($a_{12} = .135$), and the absence of such plans led to losing membership in the crowd ($b'_{12} = .053$). Thus when the response unreliability is taken out by use of the three waves, the effects are clear and consistent, showing the mutual reinforcement of college plans and membership in the leading crowd. There are two negative entries in the matrix of transition probabilities, but they do not make any of the transition rates negative. These negative entries, it should be noted, are in cells where the transition probabilities should be lowest, since it is assumed that the transition rates are zero. Thus the negative transition probabilities in these cells reinforce the contention that these transition rates are zero, and there is not simultaneous change on both attributes.

Comparison of the transition rates with the apparent transition rates from either two-wave panel shows a great deal of difference. The effects are in the same directions as those estimated from the freshman-senior panel, but the relative magnitudes are quite different. In fact, the relative sizes of the parameters of effect, the a_{ij}'s and b_{ij}'s, are almost reversed in the two cases. The largest effect, both absolutely and relative to random shocks in that direction, is the effect of college plans on gaining membership in the leading crowd ($a_{12} = .135$). The two-wave analysis, in contrast, shows this effect to be negligible.

It appears that the analysis which does not take unreliability into account, but uses only two waves, is most in error on the largest transition rates. For both the 0–1 and 0–2 analyses, the largest transition rate was q_{20}; this is reduced to the same order of magnitude as the others in the three-wave analysis, and is in fact smaller than three others. This large change is very likely due to unreliability's masquerading as change, combined with the large difference in numbers of persons giving responses 0 and 2.*

In Chap. 5, we shall examine the unreliability in college plans and crowd membership that the model has extracted out of the three-wave panel.

3. Unemployment Among Vocational School Graduates

Table 1.4 of Chap. 1 showed the relation between unemployment in the first quarter of the year after high school graduation and unemployment in subsequent quarters. In Levenson's (1963) original data, this is separated into four groups: Negro males and females and white males and females. Thus the movement toward and away from employment may be studied separately for these four groups. Table 3.6 shows the data separately for the four groups.

These tabulations will allow inferences concerning the movement of Negro and white males and females into and out of employment. However, before analyzing these data, it is necessary in this case to inquire into the meaning of "location along the v-continuum." In a situation where a stimulus evokes a response, this meaning is clear: it is the probability that the individual would give the same response if two stimuli were presented in immediate succession. It is usually impossible to carry out such measurement, because of memory traces superimposed upon the process of change; however, the conceptual meaning is clear.

There is a major difference between the unemployment data and the stimulus-response data. The observations here are observations upon a *state*, not a response, for one can assume little unreliability in reporting. The individual is either employed or not employed at a given point in time. His instantaneous probability of being employed is either 0 or 1. It is similar to

* That is, when a large difference in size of response category exists (191 vs. 96 in this case), together with unreliability, then a model of change which neglects unreliability will show that the q_{ij} from the smaller category to the larger is relatively great, so long as the marginals are to remain constant.

Table 3.6. OASI-covered employment in successive quarters following high school graduation (data from Levenson, personal communication). (1 = employed, 0 = unemployed.)

Quarter 0 *vs.* 1, 2, *and* 3

Quarter:	1		2		3	
Quarter 0	1	0	1	0	1	0
Negro males						
1	131	20	127	24	132	19
0	32	27	42	17	47	12
Negro females						
1	83	15	72	26	63	35
0	51	95	56	90	60	86
White males						
1	235	11	228	18	231	15
0	22	16	31	7	31	7
White females						
1	263	13	255	21	244	32
0	12	18	11	19	11	19

other situations in which there is little or no uncertainty between the state and the response: being married vs. being unmarried, for example. If persons were questioned at three points in time concerning their marital state, tabulations such as those of Table 3.6 might result; yet it could hardly be said that at a given point of time they were somewhere between 0 and 1 in the probability of responding "married."

Thus under such a circumstance it seems most reasonable to assume that at any point in time individuals are located at 0 or 1, and not along the continuum. This means that the present model would reduce to a regular Markov process with two states and transitions between. For data of this sort that do not conform to the simple Markov process, it seems more appropriate to use a model that assumes variation in transition rates among individuals rather than variation in location along a continuum of states. The mover-stayer model, which divides the sample into "movers" and "stayers" (see Blumen, Kogan, and McCarthy, 1955, and Goodman, 1961), is the only model of which I am aware that does this, and it has the defect of assuming two extreme types.* The present model, however, can be used with the data if we interpret the position on the ν-continuum as the probability of being employed at two points within the same quarter.

More generally, it appears that what the present model will do is separate the changes of state into two types of changes. The first type is short-term movements, into and out of employment within the same quarter-year, perhaps occurring several times during a quarter. The second is long-term movements, in which a cycle of employment–unemployment–employment occurs over a time span greater than a single quarter.

In the present analysis, the short-term changes will show up as unreliability, while the longer-term changes will show up as change. If the data were obtained at closer intervals, the apparent unreliability would be less and the change greater, for some of the short-term change would show up as actual change.

Use of Eq. (4.10) of Chap. 2 with the data of Table 3.6 allows the estimation of over-all change, $q_{01} + q_{10}$ (which will be called k, as in Sec. 1 of this chapter). The form of the equation will be similar to that used with Cohen's data, except for any two cross tabulations, at times t and τ:

$$k(t - \tau) = ln(p_{101_\tau} - p_{10}p_{1_\tau}) - ln(p_{101_t} - p_{10}p_{1_t}) \qquad (3.1)$$

The results of these computations are shown in Table 3.7. The two columns to the right show the estimated rates of movement between time periods 1 and 2 and 2 and 3.

The rates of movement shown by the different groups differ sharply—and differ as well in their stability over different times. Only among the Negro females does the same amount of movement occur between times 1 and 2 and 2 and 3. Among both Negro and white males, the movement changes less between times 2 and 3 than between times 1 and 2. Among the white females, there appears to be no movement at all.

The movement obtained between times 2 and 1 is based on the difference

* It seems more generally that there are two distinct types of behavioral data to which stochastic processes have been applied: those in which a response is measured, but the response is only loosely related to the states between which movement occurs, and those in which the state is directly measured. When a simple Markov process does not fit, then for the former type of data, models such as the present one, which assumes variation in position in some continuous space, seem appropriate. For the latter type of data, models such as the mover-stayer model, which assumes variation in transition rates or transition probabilities, seem appropriate.

Table 3.7. Movement between employment and unemployment calculated from turnover in employment, using data of Table 3.6.

	$-ln(p_{1_0 1_t} - p_{1_0} p_{1_t})$			*Movement, k*	
				$t-\tau$	$t-\tau$
for $t =$	1	2	3	2–1	3–2
Negro males	2.62	3.35	3.73	0.73	0.38
Negro females	2.12	2.49	2.88	0.37	0.37
White males	3.12	4.43	4.27	0.27	(—)
White females	3.02	3.02	3.04	0.00	0.02

between turnover in a single quarter (0–1) and turnover in a two-quarter period (0–2). The movement obtained between times 2 and 3 is based on the difference between turnover in a two-quarter period (0–2) and in a three-quarter period. This is related to the earlier discussion of short- and long-term changes. If the reinterpretation of the model's results as showing long- and short-term changes rather than change and response uncertainty, then the movement identified between times 2 and 3 is based on only those changes in which the employment-unemployment cycle is longer-term than two quarters. The movement identified between times 1 and 2, however, is based on those changes in which the cycle is longer than a single quarter. Consequently, we would expect the movement calculated between times 1 and 2 to be greater, since it includes some part of the movement that in the 2 to 3 analysis turns up as unreliability.*

An examination of the changes in Table 3.7 shows several differences between Negroes and whites and between males and females. First, the whites show much less movement than the Negroes (remembering that this disregards short-term movements in and out of employment). Second, the females show much less movement than the males. The white employment and the female employment appear to be more stable than the Negro employment and the male employment, respectively. Finally, the movement among males is estimated to be much less in the analysis using the 0–3 quarter tabulation than in the analysis using the 0–2 quarter tabulation; this is not true for females. Thus it appears that the greater movement in and out of employment among males occurs in cycles of intermediate length: the extension to three quarters does not bring in an additional set of long-term changes.

This interpretation, of course, must be rather tentative, since the model does not explicitly identify short- and long-term changes. Any strong inferences must wait until such a model, which has transition rates of different sizes, is developed.

* That this interpretation may be correct is suggested by the fact that for both Negro and white males, the 1 to 2 change is much greater than the 2 to 3 change.

Rather than studying these data again in Chap. 4 in examining response uncertainty, it is useful to calculate at this point what the "instantaneous" reliability is, since we interpret this as short-term change.

By use of Eq. (3.1) of this chapter, where $\tau = 0$, it is possible to solve for $p_{1_0 1_0}$, given the knowledge of k calculated from the 0–1 and 0–2 turnover tables. Using the above interpretation of unreliability as short-term change, we find that this shows in Table 3.8 that the white females show least short-term movement in and out of employment, while the Negro females show most.

Table 3.8. Relative amounts of movement between employment and unemployment for short-term movement.

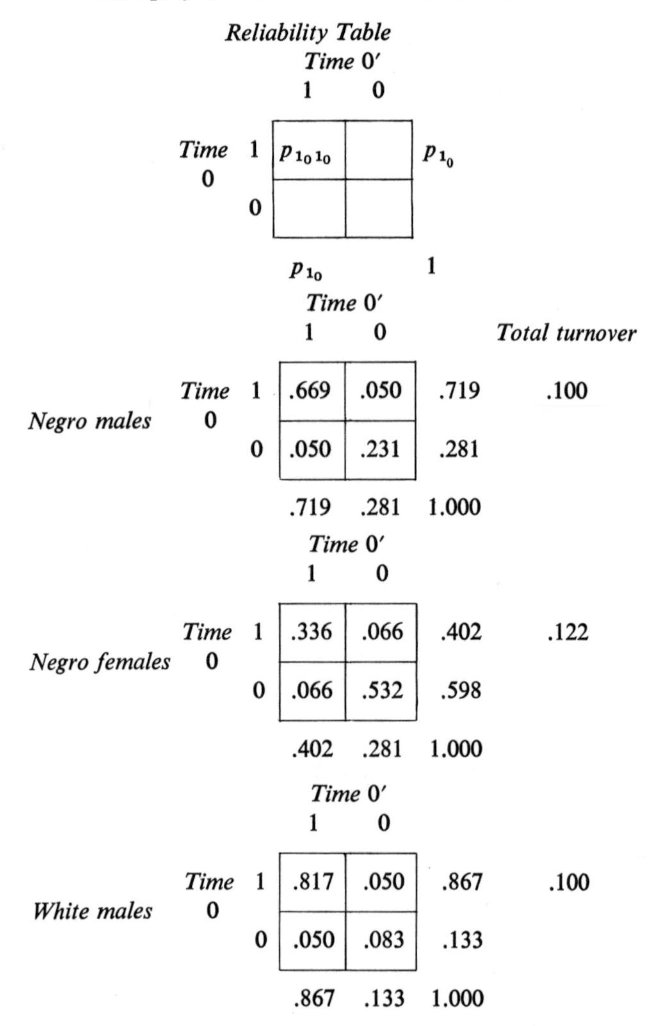

Reliability Table

	Time 0′: 1	Time 0′: 0	
Time 0: 1	$p_{1_0 1_0}$		p_{1_0}
Time 0: 0			
	p_{1_0}		1

		Time 0′: 1	Time 0′: 0		*Total turnover*
Negro males	*Time* 0: 1	.669	.050	.719	.100
	Time 0: 0	.050	.231	.281	
		.719	.281	1.000	

		Time 0′: 1	Time 0′: 0		*Total turnover*
Negro females	*Time* 0: 1	.336	.066	.402	.122
	Time 0: 0	.066	.532	.598	
		.402	.281	1.000	

		Time 0′: 1	Time 0′: 0		*Total turnover*
White males	*Time* 0: 1	.817	.050	.867	.100
	Time 0: 0	.050	.083	.133	
		.867	.133	1.000	

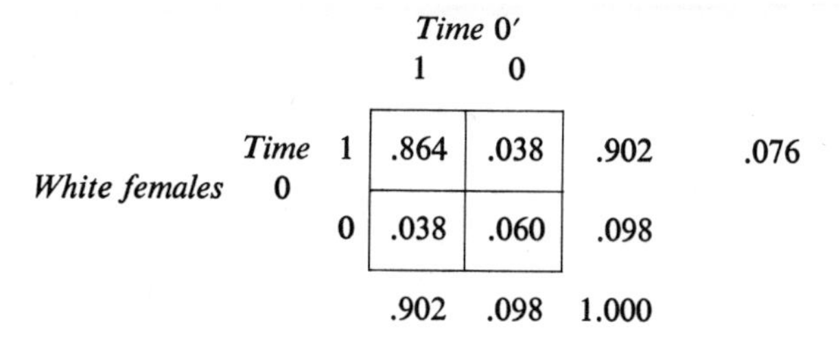

It is useful to estimate one more quantity from these data: the equilibrium proportion that would be employed if these processes continued to be governed by the same transition rates. It is evident, of course, that the processes are not constant through time; yet such a calculation will show what would be the stable levels of employment of each group if they were constant.

From Chap. 2, Eq. (4.12) may be used in conjunction with the 0–1 and 0–2 turnover tables in order to estimate the equilibrium values. These are given in Table 3.9.

Table 3.9. Employment levels at present and at equilibrium

	Equilibrium Employment (from t_0, t_1, t_2)	*Actual Employment* t_0	t_1	t_2	t_3
Negro males	.84	.72	.78	.80	.85
Negro females	.49	.40	.55	.53	.50
White males	.93	.87	.91	.91	.92
White females	—	.90	.90	.87	.83

The estimate for white females is confounded by the absence of any estimated movement at all. Using standard Markov assumptions, the estimates may easily be made from each of the three turnover tables for white females in Table 3.6.* The estimates from these three tables are .93, .83, and .76, respectively, showing that the process itself is changing, with increasing rates of movement out of employment. It is this change in the process that prevents the latent Markov process from fitting these data.

It is true, of course, that for all four groups the process is changing, so that no model that assumes constancy of the transition rates will mirror the actual processes. When changes in the process itself are as rapid as in these data, the application of such models should be accompanied by recording at shorter time intervals if the models are to be of practical value.

* An equation for estimating the steady state is

$$p_{1_e} = \frac{n_{01}/n_0}{n_{10}/n_{1.} + n_{01}/n_{0.}}$$

4. Consumer Behavior

In the study of purchase behavior with the use of this model, the two components of change and response uncertainty are very closely linked. Because of this, the examination of consumer data will be deferred until Chap. 5, when the response uncertainty results of Chap. 4 can be taken into account.

CHAPTER FOUR

The Study of Response Uncertainty in the Presence of Change

1. A Measure of Response Uncertainty

In Chap. 2, the general process of change was studied, but there was no treatment of the other part of this problem, that is, response uncertainty. One means of approaching this part of the problem is through a study of the response uncertainty that would be expected to occur if two responses were made with no separation in time. A table such as Table 4.1 would result.

Table 4.1.

		Time 0′			
		1	j ...	s	
	1	n_{11}		n_{1s}	$n_{1.}$
	⋮				
Time 0	i	n_{i1}	n_{ij}	n_{is}	$n_{i.}$
	⋮				
	s	n_{s1}	n_{sj}	n_{ss}	$n_{s.}$
		$n_{.1}$	$n_{.j}$	$n_{.s}$	n

The quantities n_{ij}/n are in this case the proportions who give response i

once and response j once when no time elapses between responses. The expected values of these quantities are $p_{i_0 j_0}$, the proportion who give response i and response j when there has been no change in any individual's position. The values in the main diagonal, $p_{i_0 i_0}$, are what is ordinarily conceived as the reliability of a stimulus. When the reliability is perfect, then all values of $p_{i_0 i_0} = 1.0$.

Such an experiment as this can almost never be carried out, because the memory of one response influences the immediately succeeding one and thus distorts the result. But the preceding analysis provides the tools necessary to carry the response at one time forward or backward to another time and thus calculate the expected values, $p_{i_0 j_0}$, $p_{i_1 j_1}$, or $p_{i_2 j_2}$.

The analysis of Chap. 2 resulted in estimation of quantities r_{ijt} and q_{ij}, based on the change that occurred between times 1 and 2. To see what is necessary for the present calculations, consider the time line below, with observations 0, 1, and 2 (not necessarily equally spaced in time).

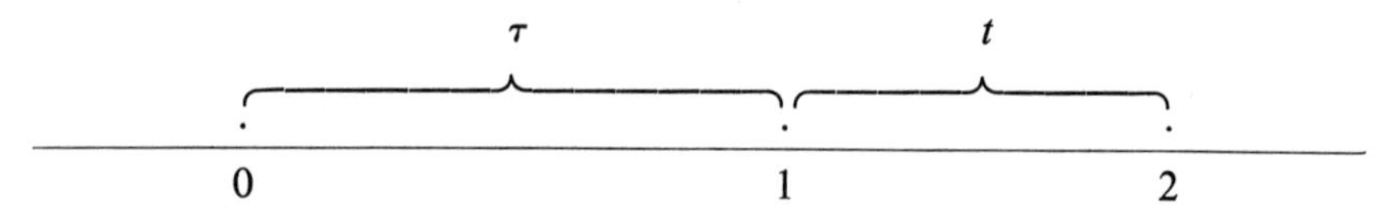

The quantities r_{ijt}, the transition probabilities over the time period t, were calculated, and from these were calculated transition rates q_{ij}. The quantities used to calculate these were estimates of $p_{i_0 j_1}$, the expected proportion giving response i at time 0 and j at time 1, and $p_{i_0 j_2}$, the expected proportion giving response i at time 0 and j at time 2 (see Eqs. (2.7) and (2.8) of Chap. 2).

The quantity r_{ijt} is a coefficient that translates a response made at time 1 to time 2. That is, r_{ijt} relates $p_{i_0 j_1}$ to $p_{i_0 j_2}$ by means of the following equation:

$$p_{i_0 j_2} = \sum_{k=1}^{s} p_{i_0 k_1} r_{kjt} \tag{1.1}$$

Suppose now that we had the values of $r_{kj\tau}$ for the time period between observations 0 and 1. It would be equally possible to translate the response made at time 0 up to time 1:

$$p_{i_0 j_1} = \sum_{k=1}^{s} p_{i_0 k_0} r_{kj\tau} \tag{1.2}$$

Equation (1.2) shows that if we had the transition probabilities $r_{ij\tau}$, it would be possible to solve the set of simultaneous equations of the form of Eq. (1.2) for values of $p_{i_0 j_0}$, in much the same way that the equations of the form of Eq. (1.1) were solved to obtain r_{ijt}.

For those who prefer to deal with operations on matrices, the problem above can be stated as follows:

$$P(0,1) = P(0,0)R(\tau)$$

To solve for $P(0,0)$, we postmultiply by the inverse of $R(\tau)$, giving

$$P(0,1)R(\tau)^{-1} = P(0,0)R(\tau)R(\tau)^{-1}$$
$$= P(0,0)$$

Thus in order to determine the response uncertainty at time 0, that is, values of $p_{i_0 j_0}$, it is necessary only to estimate the transition probabilities from time 0 to time 1, $r_{ij\tau}$. It is not possible to obtain an independent estimate of these values of $r_{ij\tau}$. They must be obtained from the previous estimates of q_{ij} or r_{ijt}. It must be assumed, therefore, that the values of q_{ij} governing the change of the elements are the same between times 0 and 1 as between times 1 and 2. With this assumption, Eq. (1.4) of Chap. 2 can be used to calculate $r_{ij\tau}$ from the values of q_{ij} and the value of τ. If the observations are equally spaced, then of course $\tau = t$, and $r_{ij\tau} = r_{ijt}$.

To obtain the response uncertainty at time 1, $p_{i_1 j_1}$, much the same procedure can be used, except that it is necessary to use the cross tabulation between times 1 and 2, which has not been utilized thus far. The entries in this table, when divided by the total sample size, n, are estimates of $p_{i_1 j_2}$. Thus it is possible to use them in conjunction with Eq. (1.3):

$$p_{i_1 j_2} = \sum_{k=1}^{s} p_{i_1 k_1} r_{kjt} \tag{1.3}$$

If the data for such a table are readily available, this is the simplest means of calculating the response uncertainty, for it uses the previously obtained r_{ijt}.

The calculation of response uncertainty at time 2, $p_{i_2 j_2}$, is somewhat more complicated than the above, because it requires calculation of backward transition probabilities, beginning again with the basic differential equations for change in v_i, Eq. (1.2) of Chap. 2. When these are integrated backward in time from τ to 0, they give, analogous to Eq. (1.3) of Chap. 2:

$$v_{i0} = v_{1\tau} r^*_{1i\tau} + v_{2\tau} r^*_{2i\tau} + \ldots + v_{s\tau} r^*_{si\tau} \tag{1.4}$$

These equations may be used in a way analogous to Sec. 2 of Chap. 2, to relate $p_{i_0 j_2}$ to $p_{i_1 j_2}$, and thus to solve for $r^*_{ij\tau}$:

$$p_{i_0 j_2} = p_{1_1 j_2} r^*_{1i\tau} + p_{2_1 j_2} r^*_{2i\tau} + \ldots + p_{s_1 j_2} r^*_{si\tau} \tag{1.5}$$

With these backward transition probabilities it is then possible to proceed as before, calculating the backward transition rates q^*_{ij} and r^*_{sjt}, and then to calculate the values of $p_{i_2 j_2}$ from $p_{i_1 j_2}$:

$$p_{i_1 j_2} = \sum_{k=1}^{s} p_{k_2 j_2} r^*_{kit} \tag{1.6}$$

Thus in any of these ways it is possible to calculate the response uncertainties, with any of the three observations as reference points. It is also possible to calculate the response uncertainties at any time θ in the future or past, $p_{i\theta j\theta}$, by calculating $r_{ij\theta}$ and $r^*_{ij\theta}$ (in matrix notation, $R(\theta)$ and $R^*(\theta)$). Then $P(\theta,\theta)= P(0,0)\,R(\theta)\,R^*(\theta)^{-1}$.

These values for response uncertainty aid in seeing what is the instantaneous interrelation between various response categories. For example, in consumer choice among brands, it appears that for many products individuals have rather stable allocations of purchases among two or more brands. For example, in purchase of coffee, one individual may buy brand 1 about two-thirds of the time and brand 2 about one-third, with no changes in his purchase probabilities, while another may buy brand 2 half the time and 3 half the time, again with no change in his purchase probabilities. Thus the first individual would contribute to $p_{1_0 2_0}$, since his $v_1 v_2 = 1/3 \times 2/3 = 2/9$. The second individual would contribute to $p_{2_0 3_0}$, since his $v_1 v_3 = 1/2 \times 1/2 = 1/4$.*

1.1. The Variance of v_i and Covariance of v_i and v_j Across Persons

The estimation of $p_{i_t j_t}$ allows the possibility of deriving the variances, $\text{Var}(v_{it})$, and covariances, $\text{Cov}(v_{it}v_{jt})$, for the distribution $f(v_1, \ldots v_{s-1}, t)$, even though the specific form of the distribution is not known. The variance of v_{it} is given by the expected value of v_{it}^2 minus the expected value squared of v_{it}, or $E(v_{it}^2) - E(v_{it})^2$. This is directly found by

$$E(v_{it}) = \int_0^1 v_{it} f(v_i)\,dv_i \qquad (1.7)$$

$$= p_{it}$$

and

$$E(v_{it}^2) = \int_0^1 v_{it} v_{it} f(v_i)\,dv_i \qquad (1.8)$$

$$= p_{itit}$$

Thus the variance of v_{it} is given by

$$\text{Var}(v_{it}) = E(v_{it}^2) - E(v_{it})^2 = p_{itit} - p_{it}^2 \qquad (1.9)$$

Similarly, the covariance of v_i and v_j is given by

$$\text{Cov}(v_{it}v_{jt}) = E(v_{it}v_{jt}) - E(v_{it})\,E(v_{jt}) = p_{itjt} - p_{it}p_{jt} \qquad (1.10)$$

* It would be of interest to factor the matrix of $p_{i_t j_t}$ by multiple-factor analysis, since the composition of $p_{i_t j_t}$ fulfills the assumptions of factor analysis rather well. In addition, the values of $p_{i_t i_t}$ are given, while they are not in the usual case. A matrix even better fulfilling these assumptions might be W, where the matrix of $p_{i_t j_t}$, P, equals e^{Wt}. The quantities w_{ij}, which are unbounded from above, could be considered linear compositions of various factors that affect the response.

Estimates of the variance and covariance may thus be made using the estimates of p_{i_t} directly from the data, and the estimates of $p_{i_t j_t}$ obtained as indicated in the preceding section. These estimates are of use as measures of the uncertainty of response and as an aid in describing the distribution of individuals, as indicated in Sec. 2.

2. The Distribution of Individuals

Response uncertainty may be described in the terms of the preceding section. However, it is often useful to go beyond this and attempt to describe the distribution of individuals at a given time *t*.

Since the position of an individual is determined by the process of change that characterizes each element within him, this process of change should itself determine the distribution of the individuals. That is, the stochastic process for the elements also describes a stochastic process for the individual characterized by the elements. Although detailed investigation of this stochastic process at the level of the individual goes beyond the scope of this book, some results may be obtained and some conjectures made in order to develop an approach to the distribution of individuals in the *v*-space.

To see first how the stochastic process at the individual level may be derived from the process at the level of elements, let us consider a two-state process for the elements, with states labelled 1 and 0. The probability of being in state 1 is v. Thus if there are m elements, the individual may be in any of $m + 1$ states at a given time. The individual is characterized by a set of probabilities, $x_0, x_1, \ldots, x_1, \ldots, x_m$, the probabilities that the individual is in state 0, 1, . . ., i, . . ., m, respectively.

As a special two-state case of Eq. (1.2) of Chap. 2, the process at the level of the elements is characterized by two transition rates:

$$\frac{dv}{dt} = -q_{10}v + q_{01}(1 - v) \tag{2.1}$$

The process at the level of the individual depends of course on the number of elements in state 1. If there are i elements in state 1, then the individual is in state i, and his transition rate out of this state is the sum of the transition rates for the elements. This is:

$$\begin{aligned} \text{toward state } i + 1 &= (m - i)q_{01} \\ \text{toward state } i - 1 &= iq_{10} \end{aligned} \tag{2.2}$$

These transition rates occur because there are $m - i$ elements yet to move to state 1, and i yet to move into state 0. The total differential equation for the change in x_i is:

$$\frac{dx_i}{dt} = -[(m-i)q_{01} + iq_{10}]x_i + (i+1)q_{10}x_{i+1} + (m-i+1)q_{01}x_{i-1} \tag{2.3}$$

That is, there is movement into this state from states $i - 1$ and $i + 1$, and movement out of it to both these states. (If state i is 0 or m, the equation is modified appropriately, because of the absence of states -1 or $m + 1$.)

The solution for this equation is given by the general solution for a set of simultaneous linear differential equations:

$$X'_t = X'_0 e^{Qt} \tag{2.4}$$

where the exponential of the matrix is defined as indicated in Eq. (1.6) of Chap. 2. The matrix Q in this case consists of the coefficients of x_i (for all values of i from 0 to m) as illustrated in Eq. (2.2). The only nonzero entries in the matrix in each row (say row i) are for columns $i - 1$, i, and $i + 1$. These three coefficients would be:

$$iq_{10} \quad -[iq_{10} + (m-i)q_{01}] \quad (m-i)q_{01} \tag{2.5}$$

The solution given by Eq. (2.4) does not provide a simple expression for the distribution of x_i, though it would be possible (for a given value of m and values of q_{ij} estimated as in Chap. 2), to obtain the vector of state probabilities X_t as a function of X_0. However, this is not a promising direction, for we do not even know the initial states X_0 for individuals.

But now we may ask a question which will give some useful insight into the structure of responses. Suppose all elements are characterized by the same probability $v_t = p_t$ of being in state 1 at time t, without regard for the individual in which they reside.* Then if each individual consists of m^* such elements, there will be a distribution of individuals, $x_0, x_1, \ldots, x_i, \ldots, x_{m^*}$ with a certain variance dependent upon the number of elements m^*. But we know from Sec. 1.1 the variance of the individuals' positions v_t to be $p_{tt} - p_t^2$. Thus we can ask what is the number of independent elements, m^*, that would produce a binomial distribution with such variance. Since the variance of the proportion of successes in a binomial distribution with mean p_t and m^* trials is $p_t(1 - p_t)/m^*$, then we can write

$$p_{tt} - p_t^2 = \frac{p_t(1-p_t)}{m^*} \tag{2.6}$$

or

$$m^* = \frac{p_t - p_t^2}{p_{tt} - p_t^2} \tag{2.7}$$

* The subscripts i used in Eq. (1.9) are deleted since this is a binomial distribution, and p_1 may be labelled p without confusion.

This result generalizes readily to the situation of a number of responses, s, and a multinomial distribution. In such a case, the hypothetical number of independent elements can be estimated for each variance and each covariance.

$$m_{ii}^* = \frac{p_{it} - p_{it}^2}{p_{itit} - p_{it}^2} \tag{2.8}$$

Since the covariance of p_{it} and p_{jt} in a multinomial distribution is $-p_{it}p_{jt}/m^*$, we obtain:

$$m_{ij}^* = \frac{p_{it}p_{jt}}{p_{it}p_{jt} - p_{itjt}} \tag{2.9}$$

These hypothetical values, m^*, are merely another way of characterizing the response uncertainty in the population. If the value of m^* is 2, for example, and the value of p_t is 0.3, this means that the responses behave as if each individual has two elements, each with probability 0.3 of being in state 1. Thus we expect that there will be .3 × .3 = .09 individuals with both elements in state 1 (persons of "type 11"); 2 × .3 × .7 = .42 individuals with one in state 1 and one in state 0 (persons of "type 10"); .7 × .7 = .49 individuals with both in state 0 (persons of "type 00"). If we obtain two responses from each of these individuals, it will be comparable to two independent samplings from individuals distributed as indicated among the three types. We would expect to find:

		Response	*Types*		
		11	10	01	00
From persons of type 11: *all respond*	1 1	.090			
From persons of type 10: .25 *respond*	1 1	.105			
.25 *respond*	1 0		.105		
.25 *respond*	0 1			.105	
.25 *respond*	0 0				.105
From persons of type 00: *all respond*	0 0				.490
		.195	.105	.105	.595

If, on the other hand, we found the indicated value, .195, for p_{tt}, then we could solve for m^*:

$$m^* = \frac{.3 - .3 \times .3}{.195 - .3 \times .3} = 2.0$$

If we took seriously such calculations of the number of independent elements governing a response, we would be forced to conclude in many cases that the number of elements was small indeed. This would lead to the conclusion, as in the above hypothetical case, that people were located at only a very few points in the space defined by $v_1, \ldots, v_s$. In the above case of two responses, and with $m^* = 2.0$, the possible locations are only $v = 0.0$, 0.5, and 1.0. There is also the difficulty posed by the fact that m^* need not be an integer when calculated from Eqs. (2.8) and (2.9).

These difficulties lead to a revision in the notion of the basic process through which these elements change. If the elements, instead of being independent, are partially dependent on the states of other elements of the host individual, then the resulting process would make possible the existence of a large number of elements together with a variance among individuals that is independent of the number of elements.

2.2. Interdependence Among the Elements

For simplicity confining our examination to the case of two states, let us now conceive of the elements changing through a somewhat more general process. Suppose, besides the exogenous probabilities of shifting from state 0 to 1 and 1 to 0, $q_{01}dt$ and $q_{10}dt$, there is an added probability, γdt, to shift to state 1 or 0 induced by each element already in that state. Thus for each element, if there are i elements in state 1 and $m - i - 1$ in state 0, the stochastic process is:

$$\frac{dv}{dt} = -[q_{10} + (m - i - 1)\gamma]v + (q_{01} + i\gamma)(1 - v) \qquad (2.10)$$

Before proceeding to examine the equation for the stochastic process at the level of the individual, it should be questioned whether the basic process of Chap. 2, Sec. 1, which assumed no interdependence among the elements, can still be used for characterizing the expected movement of the individual. This will be so only if the terms involving γ vanish.

Expanding Eq. (2.10) gives

$$\frac{dv}{dt} = -q_{10}v + q_{01}(1 - v) + i\gamma - (m - 1)\gamma v \qquad (2.11)$$

Since there are m equations for the m elements and for each of them the number of other elements in state 1 is either i or $i - 1$ (depending on its own state, and assuming there are i altogether in state 1), then there are m equations nearly identical (with m arbitrarily large, the difference becomes negligible). The value of v is i/m, since there are i elements in state 1, and thus the equation for expected change of the individual becomes (apart from these negligible differences, which vanish as m becomes large):

$$\frac{dv}{dt} = -q_{10}v + q_{01}(1 - v) \qquad (2.12)$$

This result generalizes directly to the multicategory case, so long as the contagion coefficient γ is identical among all pairs of states.* Thus the basic equations derived in Chap. 2 for the expected change in the individual, leading to the values of q_{ij} for the elements, still hold.

The transition rates at the level of the individual are, for transition out of state i $(0<i<m)$:

$$\text{from state } i \text{ to } i - i\text{: } i[q_{10} + (m - i)\gamma]$$

$$\text{from state } i \text{ to } i + 1\text{: } (m - i)(q_{01} + i\gamma)$$

The stochastic equation for change in x_i, the individual's probability of being in state i, is:

$$\frac{dx_i}{dt} = -[iq_{10} + i(m-i)\gamma + (m-i)q_{01} + (m-i)i\gamma]x_i + [(i+1)q_{10} + (i+1)(m=i=1)\gamma]x_{i+1} + [(i-1)q_{01} + (m-i+1)\gamma]x_{i-1} \tag{2.13}$$

The solution of this set of differential equations for X_t as a function of X_0 is no more helpful than for Eq. (2.2), the case of independent elements. However, at the equilibrium state, when all $dx_i/dt = 0$, the distribution is known, and depending upon the form in which it is expressed, it is known variously as the negative binomial, the limiting form of the Polya distribution, or the contagious binomial. (See Bartlett, 1955, p. 55–56, and Feller, 1943, for a discussion of contagion and the negative binomial; see Coleman, 1962, for a discussion of the above process as a contagious binomial.) The distribution of x_i at equilibrium therefore will be used for the distribution of individuals along the v-continuum, even though it is strictly legitimate to do so only when the system is at statistical equilibrium. The distribution is:

$$f(v) = f(i/m) = x_i = \frac{\binom{m}{i} \prod_{j=0}^{i-1} (a + jc) \prod_{j=i}^{m-1} [1 - a + (m-j)c]}{\prod_{j=0}^{m-1} (1 + jc)} \tag{2.14}$$

(using the convention that the first product term of the numerator equals 1 when $i = 0$, and the second equals 1 when $i = m$).†

* It would be of considerable interest to study systems in which the contagion coefficient is specific to states i and j. However, such investigation both goes beyond the scope of this book and requires additional forms of data.

† The calculation of this distribution allows an estimate of the total amount of individual change, $\Sigma|\Delta v_{it}|$, as discussed in Chap. 2, Sec. 3. Equation (2.14) gives the value of $f(v)$; hence it is possible to estimate the gross change of individuals, apart from direction. This is done by $\Sigma|\Delta v_{1t}| = \Sigma|f(v_{1t})(r_{01t} - v_{1t}(r_{01t} + r_{10t}))|$, using Eqs. (3.1) and (3.5) from Chap. 2 for the dichotomous case. Such a calculation is incorporated into the appended computer program (DICHOT) that calculates the distribution.

The parameters a and c are functions of the transition rates as follows:

$$a = \frac{q_{01}}{q_{01} + q_{10}} \tag{2.15}$$

and

$$c = \frac{\gamma}{q_{01} + q_{10}} \tag{2.16}$$

Equation (2.14) gives a distribution function derived from the process hypothesized among the elements, which allows us to describe the distribution of the individuals along the segment v, between 0 and 1. To be sure, there is no direct evidence that this distribution is in fact the one that exists, for the data are compatible with any distribution that has mean p_t and variance $p_{tt} - p_t^2$. Even if the process described by Eq. (2.14) is operative, it is known only that this distribution would result at statistical equilibrium, when $p_t = p_e$. However, in the absence of other information, and because of its relation to the hypothesized process operative among the elements, this distribution function may be used to characterize the distribution of individuals.

The mean and variance of the distribution given by Eq. (2.14) are found to be:

$$E(i/m) = a \tag{2.17}$$

and

$$E[(i/m)^2] - [E(i/m)]^2 = \frac{a(1-a)(c-1/m)}{1+c} \tag{2.18}$$

Thus since the mean of the observed distribution at time t is p_t and the variance is $p_{tt} - p_t^2$, the parameters a and c may be described in terms of these quantities:

$$a = p_t \tag{2.19}$$

and

$$p_{tt} - p_t^2 = \frac{a(1-a)(c-1/m)}{1+c} \tag{2.20}$$

Equation (2.20) may be solved for c to give $c = (p_{tt} - p_t^2 + p_t/m - p_t^2/m)/(p_t - p_{tt})$, and since m is arbitrarily large, $1/m \to 0$, giving

$$c = \frac{p_{tt} - p_t^2}{p_t - p_{tt}} \tag{2.21}$$

Alternatively, it is possible to express c as a function of the number of independent elements, m^*, given in Eq. (2.7), (2.8), or (2.9), because m^* is merely another way of expressing the variance of v. Since the variance of v in terms of m^* is $p_t(1 - p_t)/m^*$, then from Eq. (2.18) we can write

$$\frac{p_t(1 - p_t)}{m^*} = \frac{a(1 - a)(c - 1/m)}{1 + c} \qquad (2.22)$$

and letting $a = p_t$ and solving for c,

$$c = \frac{1 - m^*/m}{m^* - 1} \qquad (2.23)$$

Since m is arbitrarily large, $m^*/m \to 0$, and

$$c = \frac{1}{m^* - 1} \qquad (2.24)$$

Thus the contagion coefficient c bears a very simple relation to the number of hypothetical "independent elements," m^*.

Thus Eqs. (2.19) and (2.21) allow estimation of the parameters a and c of the distribution given by Eq. (2.14). Consequently, once having estimates of p_{tt} and p_t, it is possible to calculate this distribution. To show the form that the distribution takes for increasing values of the contagion parameter c, Fig. 4.1. shows the distribution for various values of c and $a = 0.4$. (For

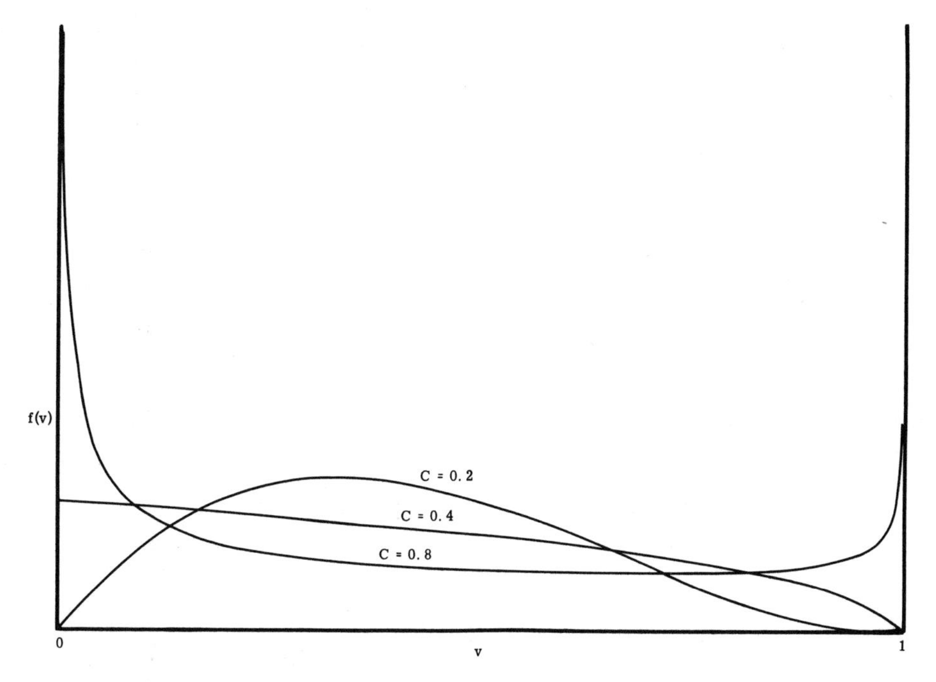

Figure 4.1. Distributions of v for a=0.4 and c=0.2, 0.4, and 0.8.

this calculation, m was taken to be 100; use of a larger value for m would change the distribution only slightly.) For aid in computation, the computer program, written in Fortran, by which the calculation of Eq. (2.14) may be carried out is given in the appendix to this chapter.

Figure 4.1 shows the various shapes that the distribution $f(v)$ may take for different values of the variance, $p_{tt} - p_t^2$. When there is little response uncertainty and the variance is large, then c is large, and most individuals are located at the extremes. When the response uncertainty is great so that p_{tt} approaches p_t^2, then the variance is small, c is small, and many individuals are located at intermediate points along v. The study of empirical data analyzed in Chap. 3 will show the distributions of individuals along v for the various situations studied.

Because of the simplicity and ease of graphical representation of the dichotomous case, it is probably wise to treat multicategory items as successive dichotomies considering $f(v_i)$ for each response category i in turn, and grouping together the other categories. However, it is also possible to show the response uncertainty of any two responses, i and j, disregarding the other categories. If we let $v_{i;j}$ represent $v_i/(v_i + v_j)$, then $f(v_{i;j})$ may be found from Eq. (2.14) by setting

$$a = \frac{p_{it}}{p_{it} + p_{jt}} \tag{2.25}$$

and

$$c = \frac{1}{m_{ij}^* - 1} \tag{2.26}$$

where m_{ij}^* is obtained from the covariance of i and j as indicated in Eq. (2.9).*

3. Individual Location Along *v*

Before studying the distributions of the empirical cases which are under analysis in this book, it is of value for us to inquire what can be said about the individual's location along v when we know his response pattern. Suppose we know that an individual in three successive observations has given response 1 each time. If we neglect any questions of change over this period, what do these responses tell us about his location? Obviously, knowing them we feel more strongly that he is somewhere toward $v = 1.0$ and away from

* It seems also that Eq. (2.14) will readily generalize to a contagious multinomial, using $a_1, a_2, \ldots, a_s$, and c as parameters in a series of s product terms in the numerator, in place of a and $1 - a$ in the two product terms of Eq. (2.14). However, use of such a distribution would seem to add little to the substantive inferences obtainable from the binomial analyses.

$v = 0.0$ than before we knew his responses. But how is this knowledge translated into a more precise statement?

This is one of those rare and fortunate circumstances in which Bayes theorem may be legitimately applied to give us the *a posteriori* distribution of this individual. For Bayes theorem is applicable when one knows an *a priori* probability distribution, then makes further observations, which modify the *a priori* distribution. In this case, the *a priori* distribution, when nothing is known about the individual's response, is given by Eq. (2.14). Bayes theorem applied to this case is:

$$f(v|k) = \frac{Pr(k|v)f(v)}{\int Pr(k|v)f(v)\,dv} \tag{3.1}$$

That is, the probability of v, given a response pattern having k positive responses, $f(v|k)$, is equal to the probability of the response pattern given v, times the probability of v, standardized by dividing by the sum of the probability of k given v times the probability of v, over the whole range of v.

These various probabilities are known, and thus the *a posteriori* probability can be explicitly calculated. For the probability of a response pattern with k positive responses and $w - k$ negative responses, given the probability v, is simply a binomial probability, $b(k;\ v,\ w) = \binom{w}{k} v^k(1 - v)^{w-k}$. In turn, the *a priori* probability of (v) is given by the contagious binomial, Eq. (2.14). Thus by the joint use of these two probability distributions as indicated in Eq. (3.1), the *a posteriori* distribution, $f(v|k)$, can be calculated.

It is possible, then, for any pattern of responses, to give this *a posteriori* distribution of the individuals who made those responses. This of course disregards any changes individuals might have made over time, and the patterns 101, 011, and 110 are all treated as identical, since only average positions over time are being treated.

To be sure, this does not give the precise location of an individual along v, but unless we have a very long sequence of his responses, it is impossible to do so. His responses only reduce the uncertainty we initially have about his position along the continuum.

The relation of Eq. (3.1) will be used in the empirical analyses of the next chapter to show the probability distribution of the location of individuals who exhibit particular response patterns. A computer program written in Fortran which will calculate the *a posteriori* distribution of an individual as a function of his response pattern is presented in the appendix.

CHAPTER FIVE

Empirical Examination of Response Uncertainty in the Presence of Change

In Chap. 3, several sets of data were studied in order to examine the change that they exhibit. These same data exhibit response uncertainty, and the developments of Chap. 4 allow the systematic study of this uncertainty. Thus in this chapter, the same data studied in Chap. 3 will be examined to extract information concerning response uncertainty. In particular, three kinds of information will be obtained for each set of data:

1. The values of $p_{i_t j_t}$, that is, the response uncertainty, when the responses that were separated in time are referred to the same point in time.
2. Information about the distribution of individuals in the space $v_1, \ldots, v_s$. This will take two forms: variances of v_i and covariances of $v_i v_j$; and then the distribution of v, assuming a particular distribution of individuals in a single dimension v_i, the contagious binomial.
3. The *a posteriori* location of individuals along the v-continuum as a function of their response patterns and of the *a priori* distribution, the contagious binomial.

1. Distortion of Judgment Under Group Pressure

In Chap. 3, Cohen's (1963) data were examined from the point of view of movement along the v-continuum between correct and incorrect responses.

Because the behavior of Cohen's subjects showed very little change after the initial few trials, the major component of the apparent changes was instead response uncertainty. Individuals behaved much as if they had a stable probability of giving a correct or incorrect response.

From the calculations of Chap. 3, it is possible to write directly the value of $p_{1_0 1_0}$, and thus to fill in the table that would result if responses could be made without intervening change. The values of $p_{1_0 1_0}$ are estimated from the intercepts in Figs. 3.3, 3.4, and 3.5, since the intercept equals $-\,ln(p_{1_0 1_0} - p_{1_0}^2)$. Since aggregation is carried out over different trials, these tables are intended to show the uncertainty not at the start of the experiment, but at any point in the experiment.

Table 5.1. Response uncertainties for Cohen's data.

all trials

Moderate

Trial 0	0′ = 1	0′ = 0	
1	.60	.10	.70
0	.10	.20	.30
	.70	.30	1.00

Extreme

Trial 0	0′ = 1	0′ = 0	
1	.72	.07	.79
0	.07	.14	.21
	.79	.21	1.00

First eighteen trials

Moderate

Trial 0	0′ = 1	0′ = 0	
1	.60	.12	.72
0	.12	.16	.28
	.72	.28	1.00

Extreme

Trial 0	0′ = 1	0′ = 0	
1	.65	.10	.75
0	.10	.15	.25
	.75	.25	1.00

Second eighteen trials

Moderate

Trial 0	0′ = 1	0′ = 0	
1	.59	.07	.66
0	.07	.27	.34
	.66	.34	1.00

Extreme

Trial 0	0′ = 1	0′ = 0	
1	.78	.04	.82
0	.04	.14	.18
	.82	.18	1.00

If there were no response uncertainty at all, if everyone were at $v = 0$ or $v = 1$, then these tables would show zeros in the minor diagonal. The size of the minor diagonal indicates the degree to which individuals are distributed along the continuum between 0 and 1. As the tables for the first and second halves of the experiments show, there was much more response uncertainty in the early part of the experiment than in the later part. Not only did persons move more during this early period, as shown in Chap. 3, but they moved from positions intermediate on the v-continuum to more extreme positions (and, interestingly, in the moderate condition, the average movement was toward incorrect, $v = 0$, while it was toward correct, $v = 1$, for the extreme condition).

This movement toward extremes is shown by the variance of p. With all at the extremes, 0 or 1, the variance of v would be $p(1 - p)$. The tabulations below show the actual variances.

Table 5.2. Variances of v for Cohen's data.

	Moderate		
	(actual)	*(binomial)*	
	$p_{1_0 1_0} - p_{1_0}^2$	$p_{1_0}(1 - p_{1_0})$	dif.
All trials	.110	.210	.100
First eighteen	.082	.202	.120
Last eighteen	.150	.224	.074
	Extreme		
	(actual)	*(binomial)*	
	$p_{1_0 1_0} - p_{1_0}^2$	$p_{1_0}(1 - p_{1_0})$	dif.
All trials	.096	.166	.076
First eighteen	.094	.188	.094
Last eighteen	.106	.148	.042

In both the moderate and extreme conditions, the actual variance in the second half of the experiment is much closer to the variance in which everyone is at $v = 0$ or $v = 1$. In the first half of the experiment, there are persons at intermediate positions, who move closer to the extreme by the second half.

The distribution of persons along the v-continuum, found from Eq. (2.14) of Chap. 4, is shown in Figs. 5.1, 5.2, 5.3, and 5.4, for the moderate and extreme conditions, and for the first and second sets of eighteen trials. In both conditions, the initial distribution is similar, with a great many persons toward the $v = 1$ extreme (the correct response), and many strewn along the continuum. But by the second eighteen trials, there is a concentration near both extremes: a greater concentration than before near $v = 1$, and a concentration also near $v = 0$. This, incidentally, roughly accords with the assumptions of Cohen's model—that there are movements into an absorbing state. Of course the present model has no absorbing states, but the movement of persons toward 0 and 1 is movement toward response certainty.

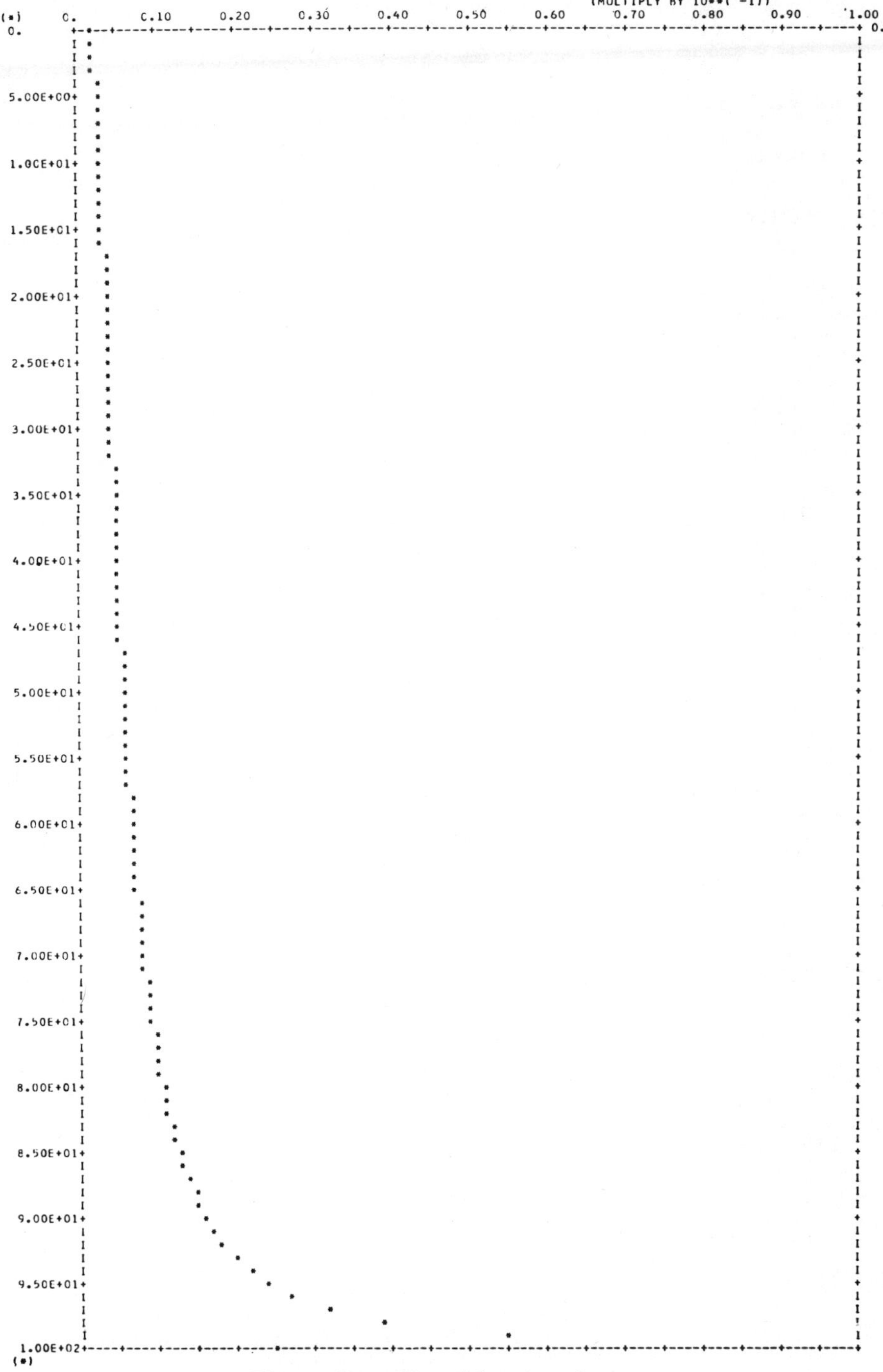

Figure 5.1. First eighteen moderate.

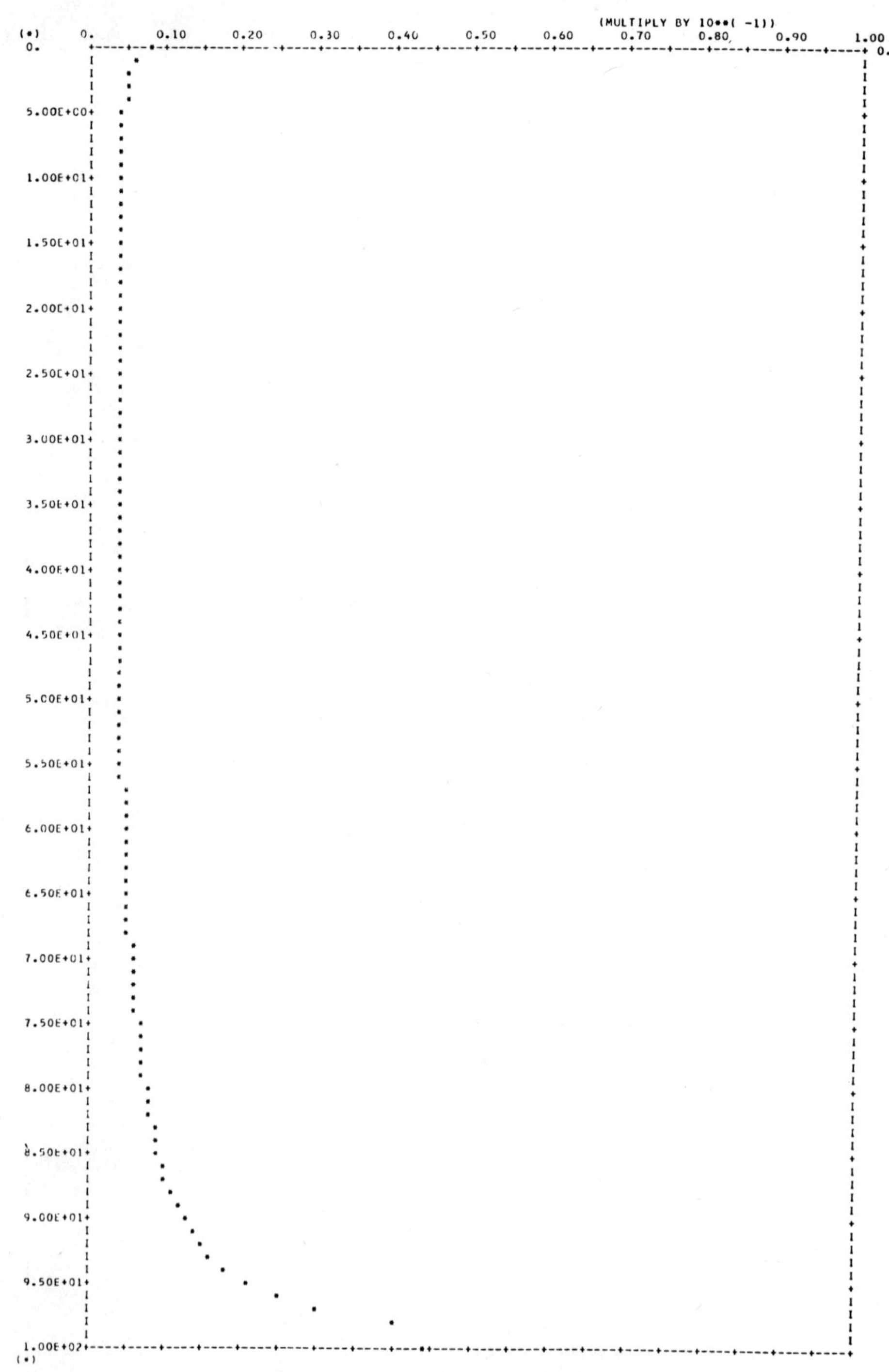

Figure 5.2. First eighteen extreme.

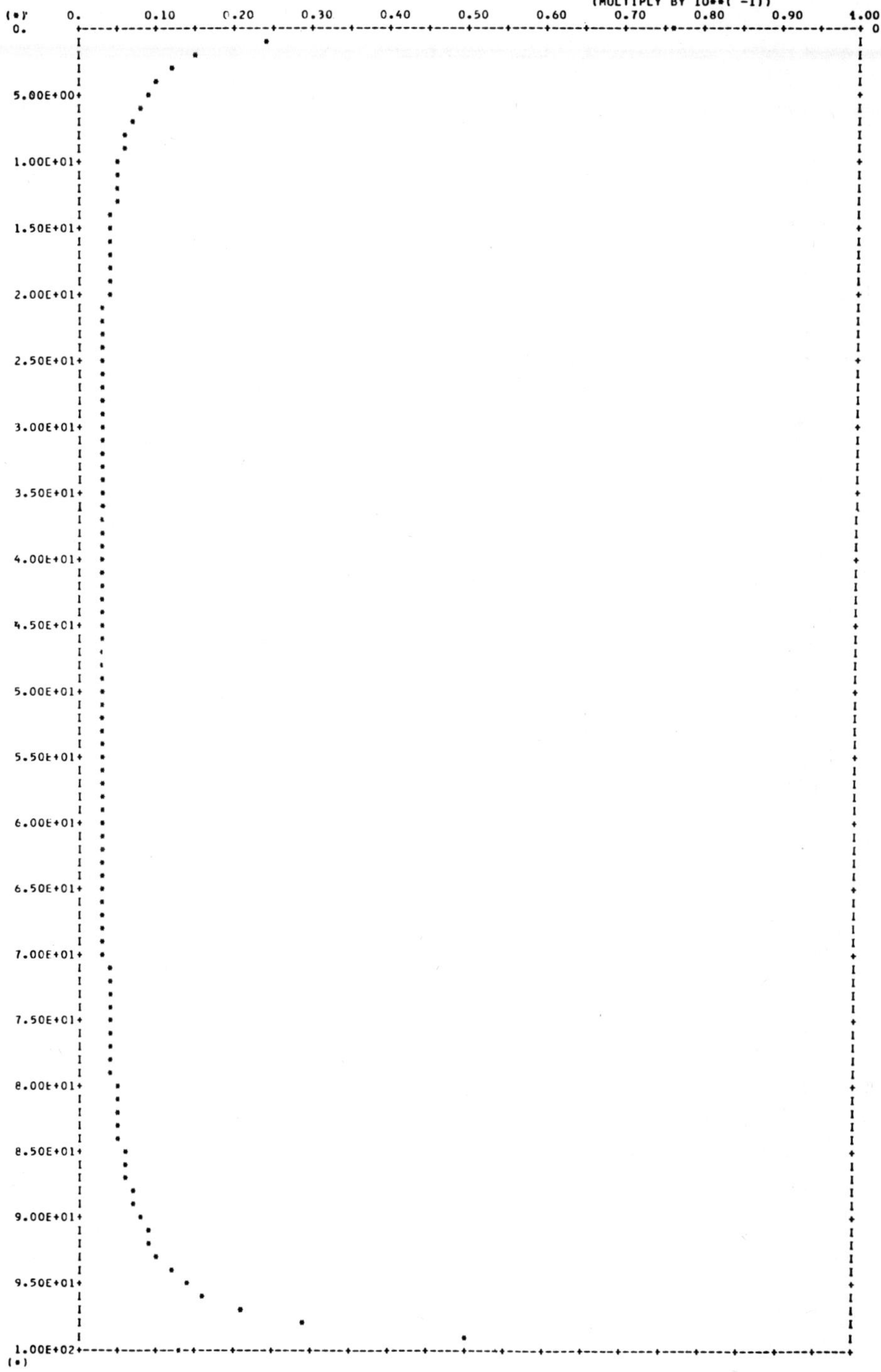

Figure 5.3. Second eighteen moderate.

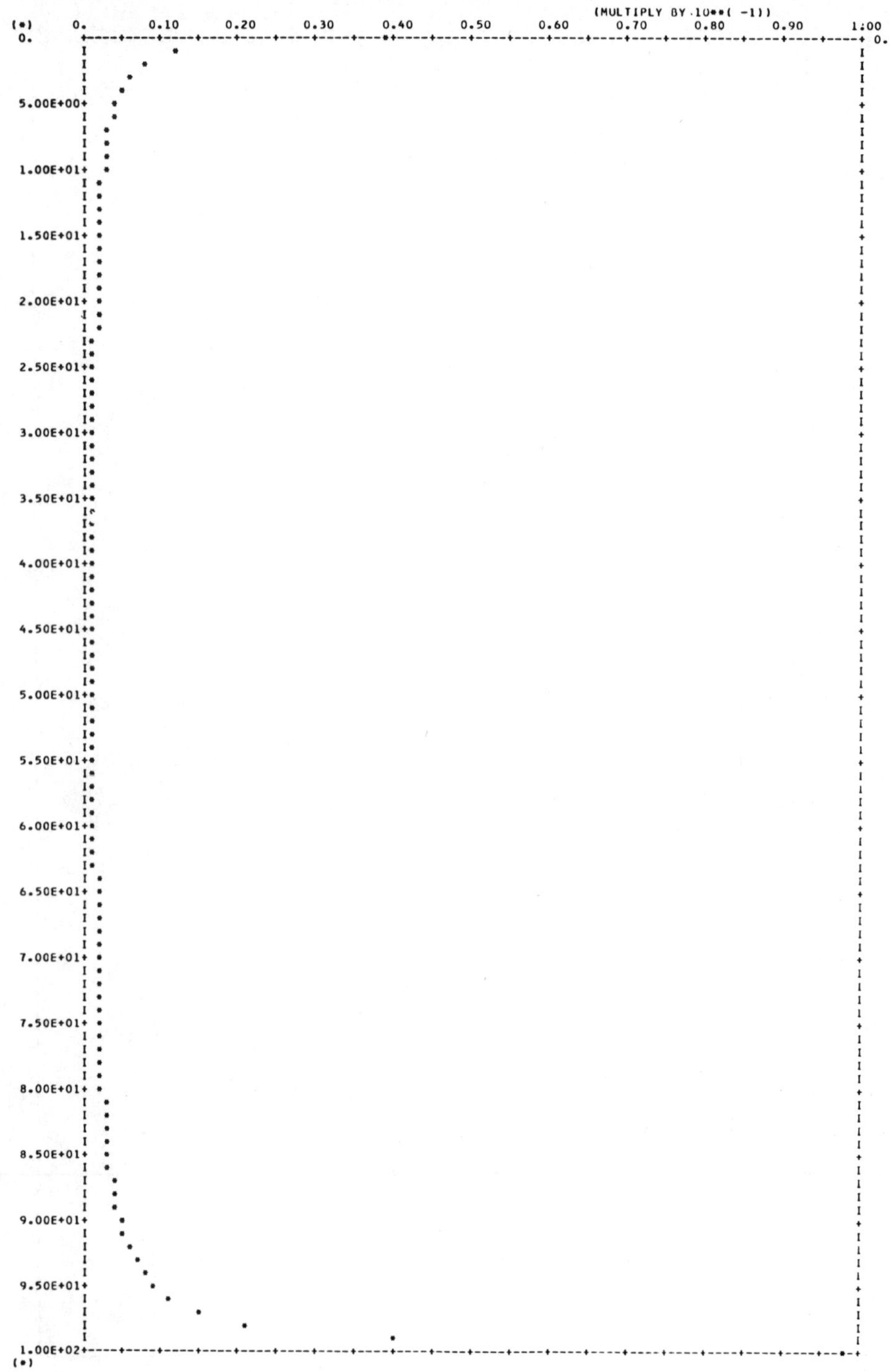

Figure 5.4. Second eighteen extreme.

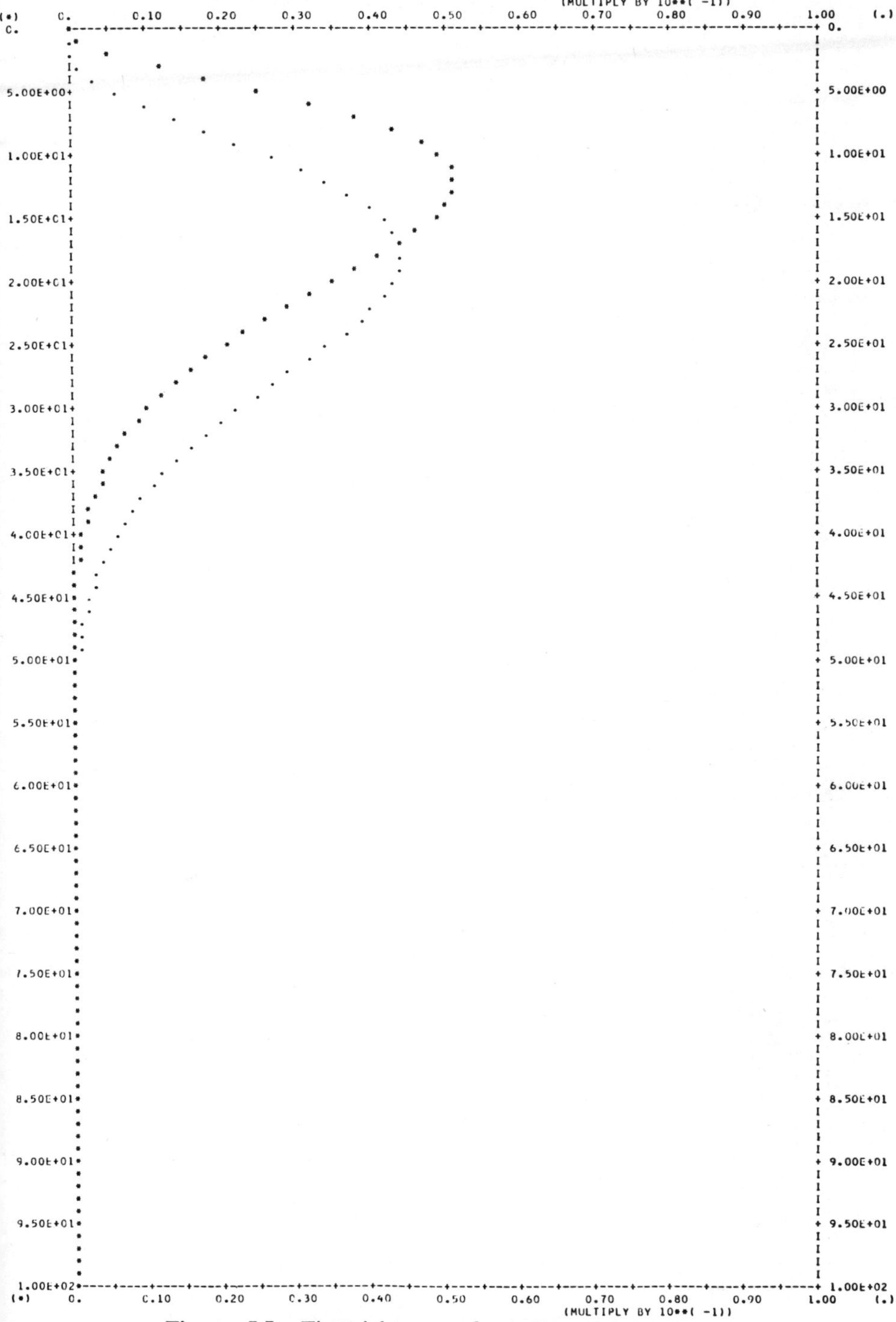

Figure 5.5. First eighteen moderate (two and three correct responses out of eighteen).

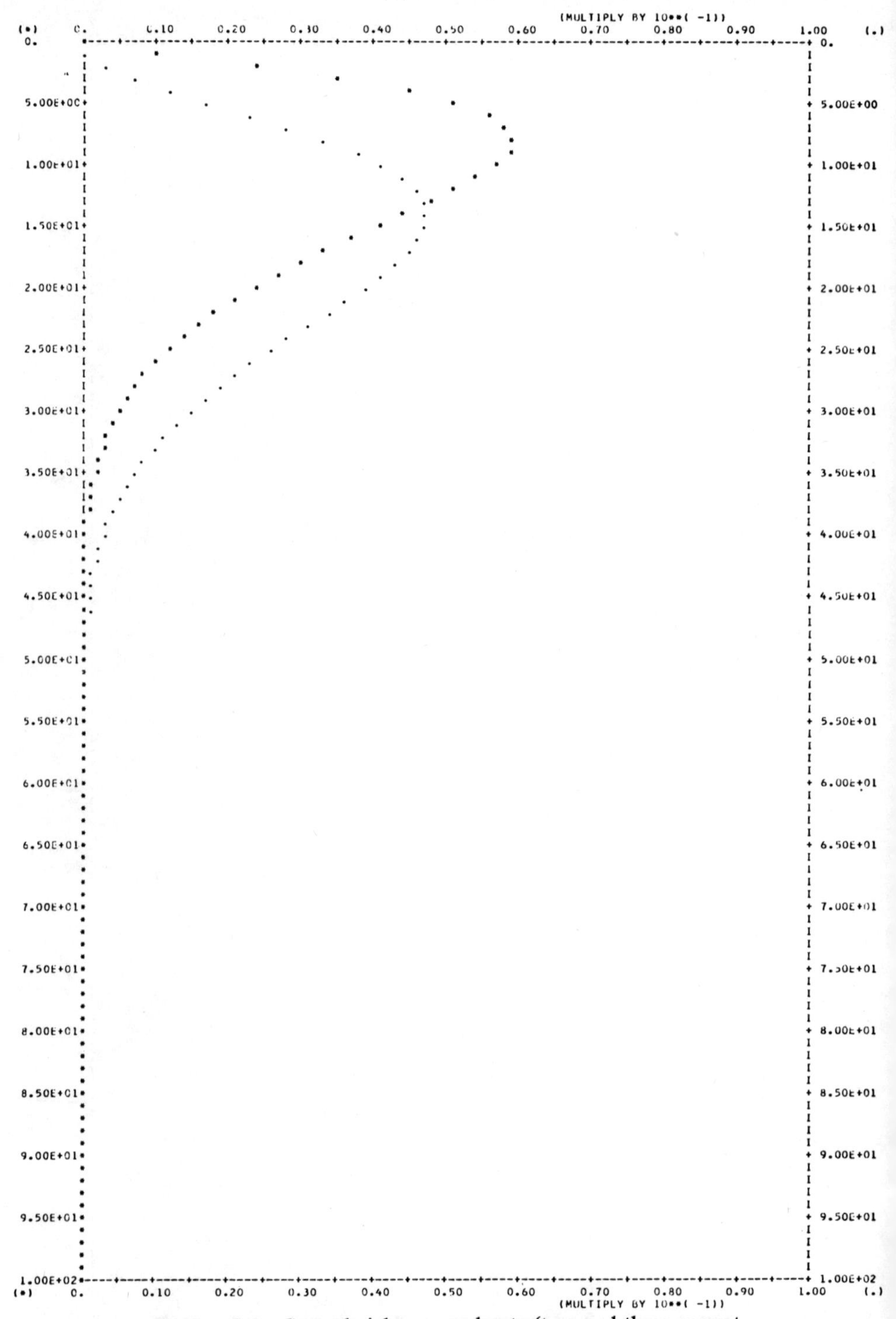

Figure 5.6. Second eighteen moderate (two and three correct responses out of eighteen).

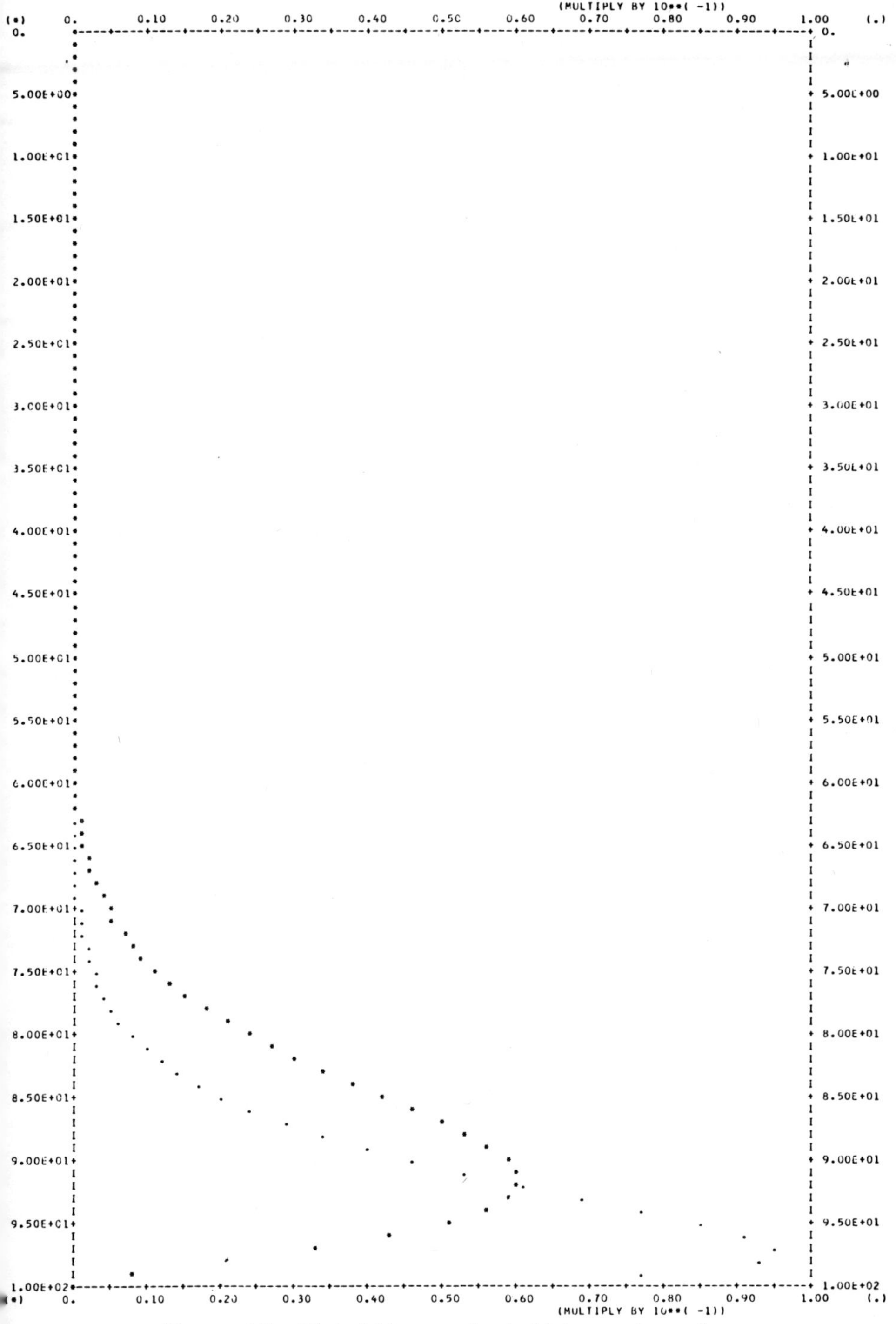

Figure 5.7. First eighteen moderate (sixteen and seventeen correct responses out of eighteen).

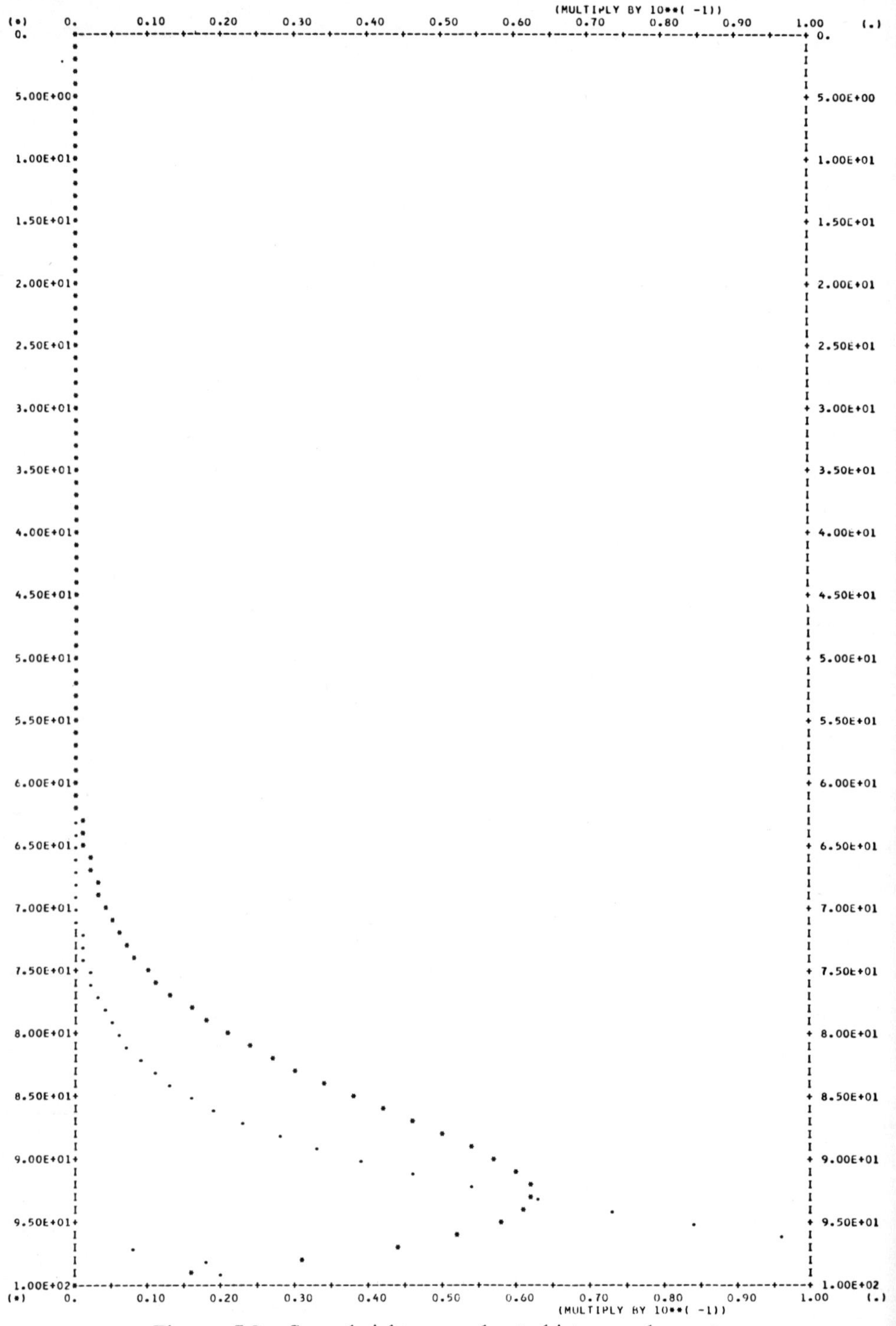

Figure 5.8. Second eighteen moderate (sixteen and seventeen correct responses out of eighteen).

Given their response patterns, the location of individuals may be found by use of these distributions together with Bayes theorem, Eq. (3.1) of Chap. 4. In estimating these locations, we neglect any movement that an individual might make, and merely ask the question, "What is the *a posteriori* distribution of individuals who give k correct responses, when we know the *a priori* distribution?"

Because of space limitations, the distributions are shown only for a small sample of response frequencies: for two and three and for sixteen and seventeen correct responses, in the moderate condition, for the first and last eighteen trials. These distributions show the probability—given that we know that a subject made two (or in general k) correct responses out of eighteen—that he lies at a given point on the continuum. As is evident from the graphs compared to Figs. 5.1 and 5.3, the *a priori* distributions, this number of responses gives a great deal of information about the individual's location.

2. Two Interdependent Attributes

The two attributes whose interdependent effects were studied in Chap. 3 may now be examined from the viewpoint of response uncertainty. The first point to examine is the response uncertainty for each separate item. This, obtained as indicated in Chap. 4 (the calculations are part of the computer program in the appendix), is as shown in Table 5.3. The table indicates that both items show some uncertainty or unreliability. Of interest is the fact that there is more response uncertainty about whether one is a member of the leading crowd than there is about college plans. This can be measured also by estimating the hypothetical number of independent elements in each response (see Sec. 2 of Chap. 4). If there were no response uncertainty, this would be equivalent to a single independent element (and the process would reduce to a simple Markov process). The number of independent elements is a measure of the response uncertainty. Using Eq. (2.8) of Chap. 4, with the information in Table 5.3, the number of independent elements is 1.4 for college plans and 1.6 for membership in the leading crowd.

Table 5.3. Response uncertainties at time 0 for college plans and membership in the leading crowd.

Membership in Leading Crowd

		0′ *Yes*	0′ *No*	
0	*Yes*	.30	.09	.39
0	*No*	.09	.52	.61
		.39	.61	1.00

College Plans

		0′ *Yes*	0′ *No*	
0	*Yes*	.42	.07	.49
0	*No*	.07	.44	.51
		.49	.51	1.00

The variance of v in the two cases is, by Eq. (1.12) of Chap. 4,

$$\text{college plans: var } v_1 = p_{1o1o} - p_{1o}^2 = 42 - .49^2 = .18$$

$$\text{leading crowd: var}(v) = p_{1o1o} - p_{1o}^2 = .30 - .39^2 = .15$$

The variance is another measure of response uncertainty; when it is zero, there is total response uncertainty; when it is at its maximum, response uncertainty is zero.

The distribution of each of these two items along the v-continuum is shown in Figs. 5.9 and 5.10. Both these graphs show the distribution at equilibrium rather than at time 0. For college plans, this is about the same as p_{1_1}, or p_{1_2}(.446); but for membership in the leading crowd, it is much higher: .628 compared to .394, .455, or .513, since there was a continual increase in the size of the leading crowd as the class progressed through school. Figure 5.9 shows the characteristic u-shaped curve that responses to attitude items appear quite generally to show. Figure 5.10 does not show this because of the skewness toward a positive response at equilibrium.

The movement of individuals in a unit of time (where the time unit is three years, between spring of the freshman year and spring of the senior year) is found as indicated in the footnote on page 65. In college plans, the average individual moved along the v-continuum, either up or down, a distance of .156. In perceived membership in the leading crowd, the average individual moved up or down .109. These averages, of course, obscure great differences between individuals, some of whom must not have moved at all, and others of whom moved from one extreme to the other. The shape of the distribution curves, with most people near the extremes, indicates that the intermediate positions are not stable ones, and that for most of those who did move, their movement covered a large part of the continuum.

Examining these two attributes together, it is possible to carry out all of the above investigations for each pair of states separately (e.g., to find covariances between each pair of states, p_{iojo} for each pair, and values of m^* for each pair). The values of p_{iojo} for all i and j can be calculated either from the 0–1 table with the appropriate transition rates r_{ij_T} (using Eq. (1.2) of Chap. 4) or from the 0–2 table (using transition rates r_{ij_T+t}). The latter will generally be less accurate, because the translation backward by use of r_{ij_T+t} is over a longer time span. This can be seen in Table 5.4, where tables of values of p_{iojo} and covariances calculated from the 0–1 and 0–2 tables are presented. The former values of p_{iojo} show two very small negative values (which arise from lack of fit of the model to the data); but the latter values of p_{iojo} show four negative values, which are larger.*

* This lack of fit arises from the constraints placed on the q_{ij}'s, setting $q_{30}, q_{03}, q_{21}, q_{12}$ equal to zero. If the transition rates were unconstrained, the values of p_{iojo} from the two tables would be identical.

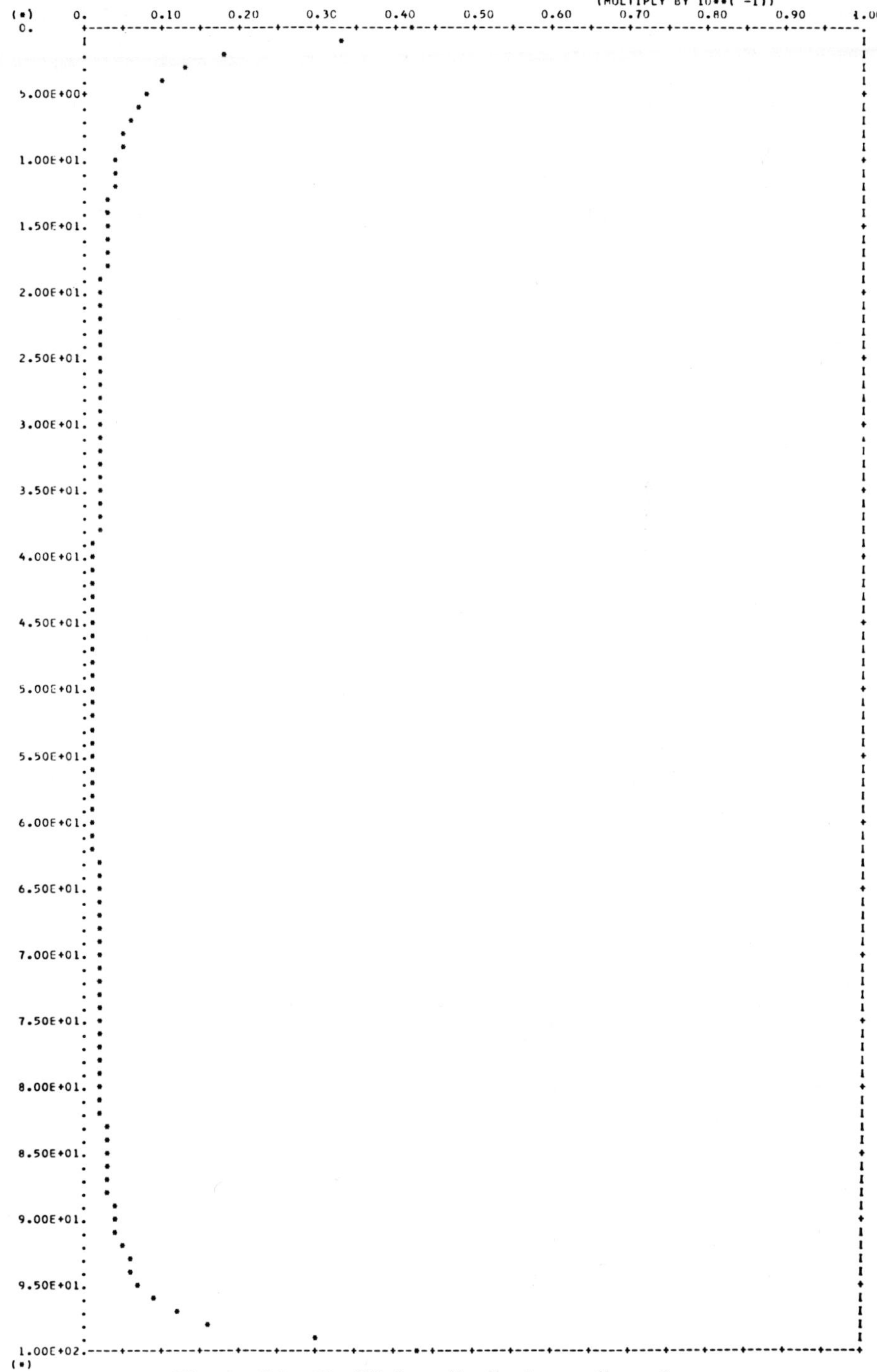

Figure 5.9. Equilibrium distribution: college plans.

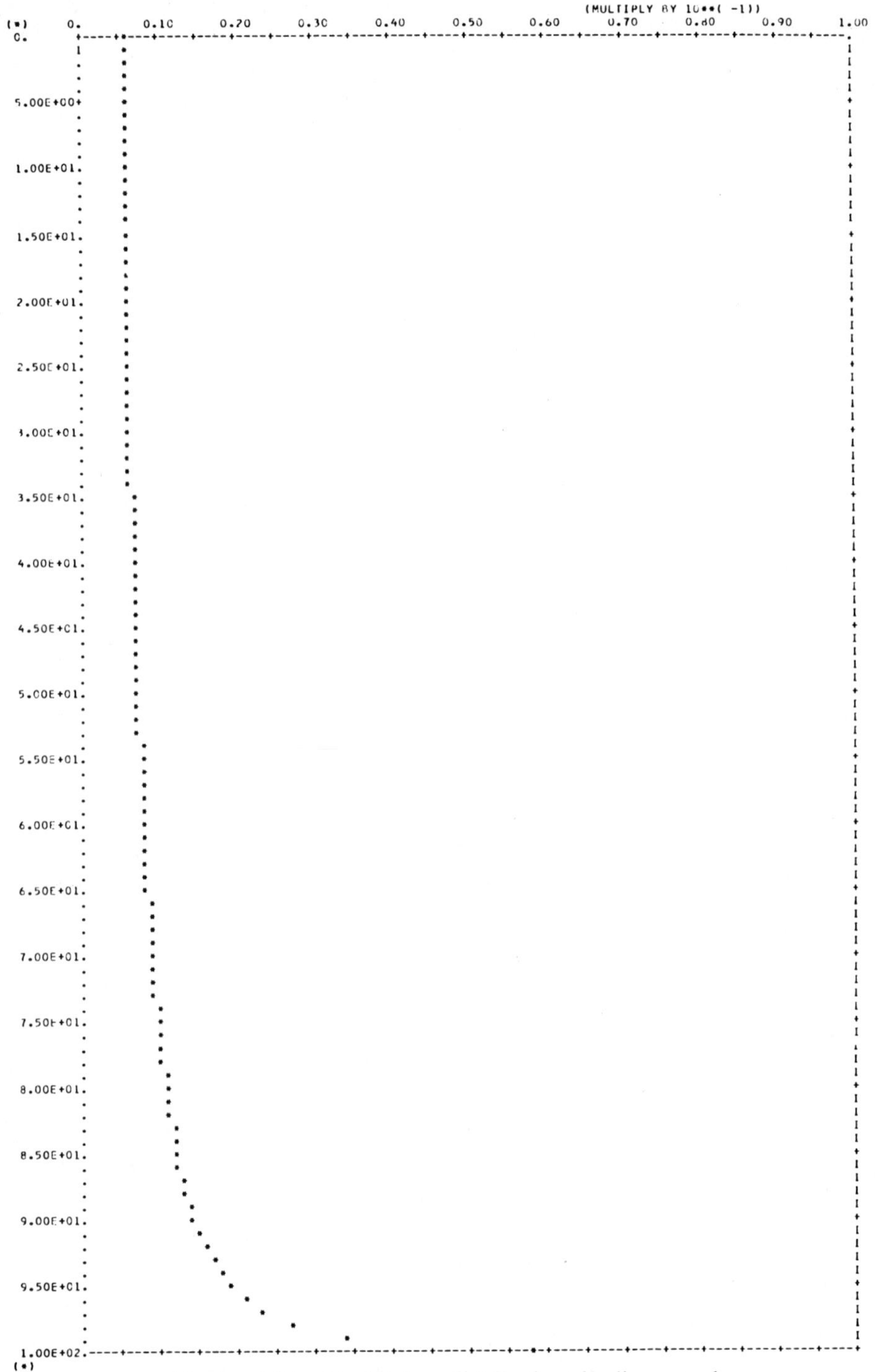

Figure 5.10. Equilibrium distribution: leading crowd.

Table 5.4. Response uncertainties and covariances for college plans and membership in the leading crowd.

From 0–1 *table*

Response Uncertainties $p_{i_0 i_0'}$

Time 0 \ Time 0′	3	2	1	0	
3	.159	.037	.026	.001	.223
2	−.001	.124	−.002	.050	.171
1	.022	.010	.196	.037	.265
0	.012	.056	.009	.264	.341
	.192	.227	.229	.352	1.000

Covariances

	3	2	1	0
3	.110	−.001	−.034	−.075
2	−.039	.095	−.048	−.008
1	−.038	−.034	.125	−.053
0	−.064	−.002	−.082	.148

From 0–2 *table*

Response Uncertainties $p_{i_0 j_0}$

Time 0 \ Time 0′	3	2	1	0	
3	.148	.039	.014	.022	.223
2	−.005	.139	−.022	.059	.171
1	.015	.015	.185	.050	.265
0	−.011	.060	−.012	.304	.341
	.147	.253	.165	.435	1.000

Covariances

	3	2	1	0
3	.099	.001	−.045	−.054
2	−.043	.110	−.067	.001
1	−.044	−.030	.115	−.041
0	−.086	.001	−.102	.188

Because of the fact that these tables are composed of two dichotomous items, the tables of response uncertainties and covariances are not as useful as in other instances. If this were a single, four-category item, the values of p_{iojo} and $\text{cov}(v_i,v_j)$ would show how "close" the responses in the two categories i and j are.

3. Consumer Behavior

Data of the type shown in Tables 1.1 and 1.3 are regularly gathered by several commercial diary panel organizations; and for special purposes, such panels are often set up by market research agencies. The data are collected through purchase diaries kept by housewives and mailed to the agency at intervals.

In conjunction with this model, such data can be used to study several facets of purchase behavior. One is the general notion of "brand loyalty," by which several things, often confused with one another, are meant. First, considering no processes of change whatsoever, brand loyalty can be examined as response reliability. That is, if by experiment one could take a set of housewives on two shopping trips in immediate sequence, without the first set of purchases affecting the second set, what would the brand reliability be in their purchase behavior? These reliabilities can be estimated by the values of p_{ioio} estimated from the present model. In addition, one can measure just how close two particular brands are to one another, in the sense that a person is likely to purchase one on one trip and the other on the next trip (again assuming no effects of the first purchase on the second). This is estimated by the size of p_{iojo}. (As a measure of reliability, the values p_{ioio} should be divided py p_{io}, and the values p_{iojo} by $\sqrt{p_{io}p_{jo}}$.)

Such "purchase reliability" can also be expressed through the distribution of individuals in the space of $(v_1, v_2, \ldots, v_s)$. The distribution function for this multidimensional space was not developed in Chap. 4, and thus the distribution function for the single dimensional space must be used. This may be used for any partitioning of the initial data into a fourfold table. The partitioning of most interest, of course, is that which successively examines each brand vs. all others. However, families of brands may be examined together to study the distribution of persons between the two families of brands. For example, there may be a great polarization between purchasers of Ford Motor Company automobiles and General Motors automobiles, with much purchase unreliability within each of these two families.

In addition to purchase reliability, discussions of brand loyalty also are usually concerned with "brand switching," where the switching is viewed not as a manifestation of purchase unreliability, but as an actual change that will tend to persist in later purchases. Of course what is mere unreliability from the point of view of a long time span may be changes that persist when considered over a much shorter time span. When the time span covers several purchases, however (which is generally the time span of interest), then with most data that have been scrutinized, some of the switching is change that persists. It becomes of interest, then, to see in a given market just how much such change is occurring, how much movement there is of the sort that can be isolated as change in position in the v-space.

These, then, are two aspects of brand loyalty that can be studied with the present model. One other kind of behavior, however, cannot. Sometimes it is believed that "one purchase leads to another," that a purchase of a brand will bring a successful experience and thus lead to another purchase. Such effects undoubtedly exist for new products in a market or for persons who are entering a market and gaining initial experience with the products. They are probably less true for persons and brands in a stable market situation.

The model developed here does not include such effects. The response (in this case, a purchase) is assumed to have no effect on the individual's position. The response is merely an indicator of that position, which is affected by exogenous factors.*

In addition to the study of brand loyalty, such diary panels can be useful for predicting the equilibrium brand share of a new brand. When a new brand comes into the market, it often spurts up very rapidly at the beginning, only to fade out after a short time. This is often because persons buy once but do not repurchase, and even though the product gets no repeat purchasers, it grows in sales for some time until it has exhausted the potential pool of customers.†

* It is not clear just how models with these two differing assumptions would be distinguished, so long as responses were regularly spaced. If they were not, a model that treated the purchase as having a positive effect on further purchases would predict more change in a given period of real time when purchases were more frequent, while one that viewed the response as a mere manifestation of a state (as does the present model) would predict no difference in the rates of change.

† There are certain items that are one-time-only purchases, and their sales curves indicate the extreme of this. Popular records and books are two of the best examples: though no one makes a second purchase of the same record or book, their sales curves rise until finally they must fall, as the pool of customers is exhausted.

Such repurchase behavior can be seen from the estimated transition matrices for an ordinary Markov process. However, the simple Markov process is unable to separate the actual change from unreliability of purchase—and it is thus unable to differentiate between a case in which the new brand has captured a small but loyal group and a case in which it is attracting a larger but less loyal following. Such a difference becomes evident upon examining the distribution of persons along the v-continuum; a new brand may be gaining its purchasers through moving a large number of persons part of the way along the continuum from $v = 0$ to $v = .2$ or $.3$; or it may be gaining through moving a few nearly all the way, to $v = .8$ or $.9$. Obviously its ultimate share of the market and the speed with which it may be expected to reach this share will depend on how it is gaining its purchasers.

The data presented in Table 1.4 may be studied by the methods described in Chaps. 2 and 4. In these data, two brands, 8 and 10, were entering the market for the first time. A diary panel was established, covering a 182-day period, and the data shown in Table 1.4 are aggregated from that panel. Each customer had a sequence of purchases, and as with the Cohen data, aggregation was carried out over both time and individuals. The aggregation over time is unfortunate, for it obscures the very changes in market share that are of interest. Its necessity arises from the fact that the frequency of purchase of the new brands is so low in early periods as to be subject to large influences from random fluctuation. The change, of course, will not be totally obscured, because the aggregation over time does not destroy the time asymmetry, and a gain in purchases will be accurately reflected in the data.

The data in Table 1.4 are for purchases x, $x + 4$, and $x + 8$, that is, observations separated by three intervening purchases. In Table 5.5 are presented data for three other spacings of observations:

x, $x + 2$, $x + 4$ (one intervening purchase)

x, $x + 3$, $x + 6$ (two intervening purchases)

x, $x + 5$, $x + 10$ (four intervening purchases)

Initially, it was attempted to study this behavior simply by cross tabulation of purchases x, $x + 1$, and $x + 2$. However, one element in purchase behavior for this item prevented this: repurchase of the same brand was *less* likely for adjacent purchases than for purchases separated by one remove. A purchase apparently had an effect on the subsequent purchase, *inhibiting* it. This appears to be true with a number of product classes where two or more brands are consumed simultaneously (breakfast cereal is the best example). In such cases the most recently purchased brand will not need replenishing as soon as the brand purchased earlier, thus superimposing a

Table 5.5. Purchases of a grocery item from among eleven brands.

Brand of purchase x + 2

Brand of purchase x	1	2	3	4	5	6	7	8	9	10	11	*Total*
1	217	22	19	8	9	19	15	29	38	19	2	397
2	26	89	8	5	1	3	3	7	17	2	4	165
3	25	5	164	15	4	13	13	35	41	4	7	326
4	18	2	17	94	10	7	16	24	21	6	2	217
5	12	4	10	13	77	4	11	8	17	5	2	163
6	16	4	12	7	4	47	7	10	15	5	12	139
7	20	4	21	14	10	6	85	25	41	13	4	243
8	25	6	30	14	5	5	24	336	47	17	3	512
9	31	19	36	22	19	20	42	29	286	20	14	538
10	12	2	9	1	3	6	5	18	17	60	3	136
11	4	2	8	0	2	12	5	6	10	5	20	74
Total	406	159	334	193	144	142	226	527	550	156	73	2910

Brand of purchase x + 4

Brand of purchase x	1	2	3	4	5	6	7	8	9	10	11	*Total*
1	190	20	33	11	11	18	16	35	39	20	4	397
2	28	91	6	7	1	2	3	7	15	2	3	165
3	26	4	143	14	5	13	17	43	43	11	7	326
4	17	3	17	83	12	7	14	26	29	4	5	217
5	16	2	14	6	61	5	17	16	20	4	2	163
6	23	2	15	7	1	44	5	9	18	6	9	139
7	17	6	19	11	13	9	82	39	32	11	4	243
8	22	3	35	21	13	12	30	310	43	16	7	512
9	39	16	36	21	30	24	34	37	268	20	13	538
10	16	1	5	2	6	7	7	19	12	57	4	136
11	6	1	6	0	1	12	4	8	8	6	22	74
Total	400	149	329	183	154	153	229	549	527	157	80	2910

Brand of purchase x + 3

Brand of purchase x	1	2	3	4	5	6	7	8	9	10	11	*Total*
1	151	18	18	8	7	12	12	30	34	11	5	306
2	22	71	4	4	2	1	0	6	8	2	3	123
3	21	3	111	8	3	9	8	31	26	6	5	231
4	13	5	11	63	10	3	15	18	11	7	1	157
5	6	3	6	7	56	7	10	5	13	1	0	114
6	12	1	10	3	1	28	1	3	20	5	6	90
7	12	5	12	5	11	3	58	32	29	7	0	174
8	14	3	31	17	6	8	15	226	25	13	1	359
9	26	12	27	14	13	16	26	31	197	10	9	381
10	15	1	5	2	2	4	2	7	7	44	4	93
11	1	0	7	0	1	5	3	4	8	6	14	49
Total	293	122	242	131	112	96	150	393	378	112	48	2077

Brand of purchase x + 6

Brand of purchase x	1	2	3	4	5	6	7	8	9	10	11	*Total*
1	134	15	20	5	10	18	13	34	35	20	2	306
2	27	65	3	5	0	2	0	7	12	0	2	123
3	22	6	92	9	1	9	9	38	35	5	5	231
4	11	1	23	61	7	4	9	19	14	5	3	157
5	10	0	6	10	45	7	13	8	12	2	1	114
6	16	4	7	6	1	29	1	2	13	4	7	90
7	19	2	7	6	10	5	57	33	27	5	3	174
8	21	2	25	17	10	4	21	220	15	16	8	359
9	22	15	33	14	19	19	23	30	182	17	7	381
10	15	1	7	3	1	4	5	12	5	37	3	93
11	4	2	5	0	0	5	1	8	8	2	14	49
Total	301	113	228	136	104	106	152	411	358	113	55	2077

Brand of purchase x + 5

Brand of purchase x	1	2	3	4	5	6	7	8	9	10	11	*Total*
1	73	11	12	2	4	10	5	17	17	12	2	165
2	12	37	1	3	2	1	1	4	6	1	0	68
3	14	4	55	5	2	5	2	21	14	3	1	126
4	4	0	7	37	2	4	1	11	10	2	0	78
5	3	0	2	3	26	1	5	4	5	2	2	53
6	7	0	3	2	0	10	0	2	5	3	4	36
7	8	1	4	4	5	2	27	14	17	2	0	84
8	5	3	9	8	3	3	1	101	7	6	1	147
9	18	5	20	4	7	3	10	18	99	11	5	200
10	9	0	4	0	3	3	1	7	2	21	2	52
11	1	1	5	0	0	1	0	3	4	3	7	25
Total	154	62	122	68	54	43	53	202	186	66	24	1034

Brand of purchase x + 10

Brand of purchase x	1	2	3	4	5	6	7	8	9	10	11	*Total*
1	66	8	7	6	5	12	6	22	18	13	2	165
2	14	35	1	2	1	1	0	6	5	1	2	68
3	14	5	45	4	1	4	2	22	25	1	3	126
4	2	1	11	31	6	2	3	9	9	4	0	78
5	7	2	3	6	14	1	5	7	6	1	1	53
6	4	2	4	1	1	9	3	0	7	2	3	36
7	11	0	6	2	6	2	25	19	11	2	0	84
8	4	1	7	9	4	4	6	97	8	5	2	147
9	25	9	16	8	5	5	16	21	84	7	4	200
10	8	0	11	0	2	1	2	5	5	17	1	52
11	3	0	2	1	0	1	2	4	4	1	7	25
Total	158	63	113	70	45	42	70	212	182	54	25	1034

cyclical pattern on the processes under study here. As a consequence, the processes of change and purchase reliability are obscured.

Despite such a pattern (which is not completely erased by skipping purchases, for Table 5.5 shows some diagonal entries that increase for the longer time span), these data were analyzed both to examine patterns of brand loyalty and to examine projections in the market share of the two new brands. From the tabulations shown in Table 5.5, purchase reliabilities and the probabilities of buying each other brand were calculated. For the four sets of data, the purchase reliabilities $p_{i_0 i_0}/p_{i_0}$, for all brands, are shown in Table 5.6. (These were calculated from the total matrix, but the reliabilities based on dichotomizing each brand vs. all others are nearly identical to these.)

Table 5.6. Purchase reliabilities for eleven brands based on four cross tabulations of purchases.

Brand	*Purchases skipped* 1	2	3	4	*Current Brand share* p_{i_0}
1	.63	.56	.54	.48	.136
2	.53	.63	.63	.56	.057
3	.58	.58	.58	.50	.112
4	.49	.41	.43	.57	.075
5	.60	.61	.50	.98	.056
6	.36	.30	.26	.30	.048
7	.37	.33	.22	.34	.084
8	.72	.66	.71	.72	.176
9	.57	.56	.58	.57	.185
10	.46	.56	.42	.50	.047
11	.24	.29	.52	.28	.025

There is some fluctuation among the estimates from the different sets of data, caused in part by the superimposed cyclical pattern. However, certain brands stand out as having particularly high or low purchase reliabilities. Brand 8, one of the two new brands, has the highest reliability, about .7; brand 2 has the next highest, about .6 (disregarding the deviant value of .98 for brand 5). The lowest are brands 6, 7, and 11 (all around .3), and then brands 4 and 10 (between .4 and .5). The purchase reliability is related, as it should be, to brand share, with the brands having highest brand share also having higher purchase reliabilities. However, some brands are quite deviant from this pattern: brand 2 has the second highest reliabilities, but is seventh in brand share; brand 7 has the second lowest reliabilities, but is fifth in brand share. The two brands with highest brand share, 8 (a new brand) and 9, are quite different in their purchase reliabilities. The two new brands, 8 and 10, differ sharply in their purchase reliabilities, brand 8 having the most reliable purchasers, and brand 10 having purchasers of only average reliability.

This reliability may also be expressed by a distribution along the v-continuum. One such distribution for the most reliable brand, 8, is shown in Fig. 5.11. The graph is shown by *; accompanying this graph is a chart (represented by ·) showing the decay in repurchase probability over time, from .7 at t_0, to about .18 after 100 purchases.

The other aspect of brand loyalty, movement over time toward or away from the brand, is best studied by examining the expected average movement of the individual for each brand. This movement was calculated for only the four dominant brands, and their movement is shown in Table 5.7.

Table 5.7. Expected movement between adjacent purchases, Δv_{it}, averaged over all individuals.

$Av(\Delta v_{it})$

Purchases skipped

Brand	1	2	3	4
1	.017	.012	.009	.007
3	.014	.012	.011	.006
8	.016	.004	.004	.004
9	.008	.006	.007	.011

$Av(\Delta v_{it})$ *not standardized to the same time unit*

Purchases skipped

Brand	1	2	3	4
1	.034	.036	.036	.034
3	.028	.036	.044	.030
8	.032	.012	.016	.022
9	.016	.018	.028	.053

In every case except brand 9, the estimate of the movement between purchases declines as the gap between observations increases. This movement was estimated as indicated in the footnote, p. 65. However, such an estimate includes, for the shorter time periods, some changes that within the longer period, have been cancelled out by reverse movements. Thus the apparent change *per purchase period* will likely be less because of such effects. For this reason, the average movement over the total time period is also included in Table 5.7 (for each of the calculations, it is 2, 3, 4, and 5 times the interpurchase movement, respectively). An examination of these calculations suggests that the total movement increases only slightly as the time interval increases—though not enough to make the interpurchase movement, shown in the upper half of the table, constant.

It is evident that such processes require further study with data on larger samples and less confounded by the cyclical pattern that overlays the process of change under study.

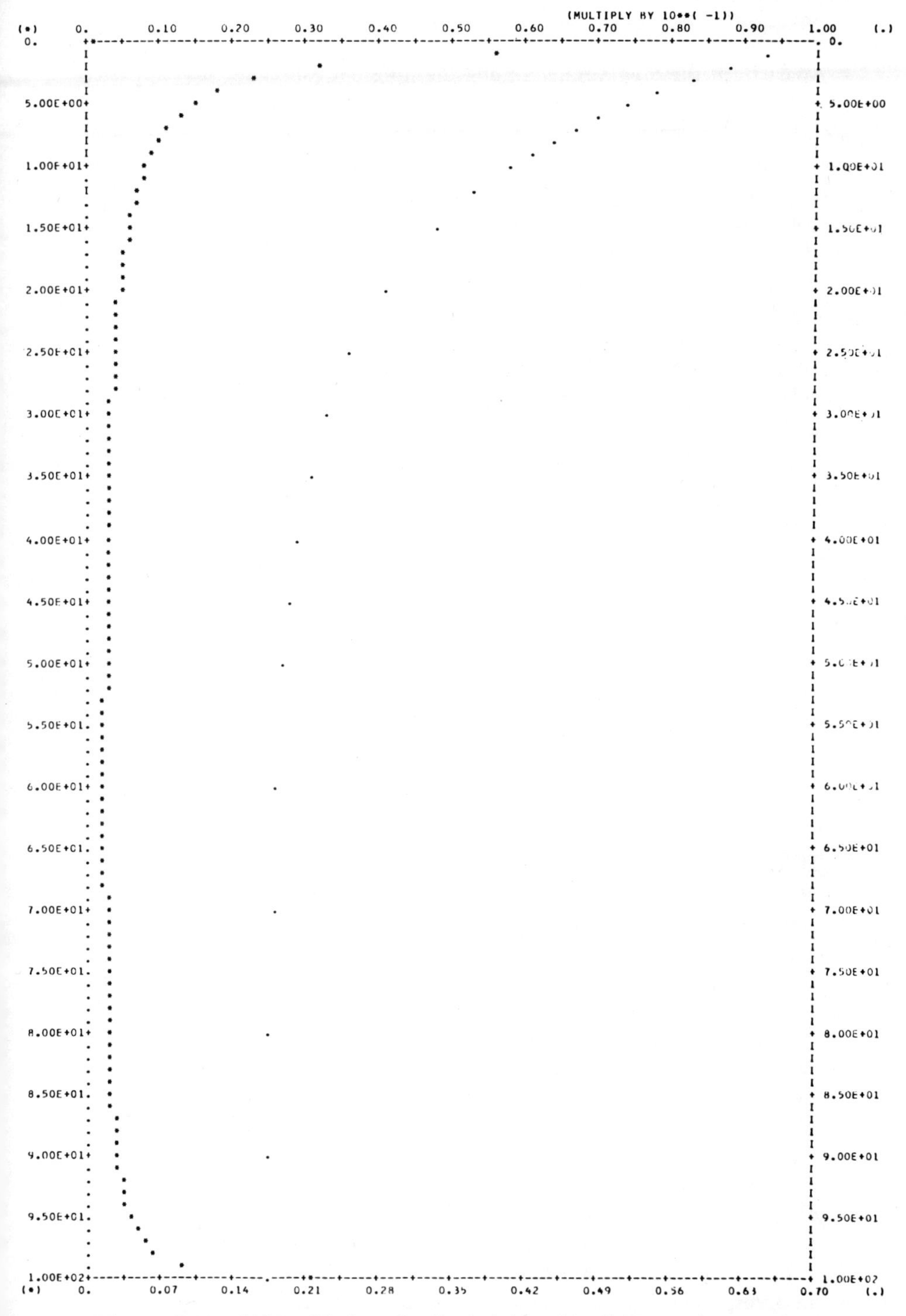

Figure 5.11. "*"Equilibrium distribution: brand 8. "·"Decay in repurchase probability: $p_{i_0 i_t} / p_{i_0}$ vs. t.

Apart from these variations among the different estimates, it is apparent that purchasers move least with respect to brands 8 and 9. As Table 5.6 showed, 9's purchase reliability is not particularly high; but apart from such purchase-to-purchase unreliability, the movement toward and away from the brand is quite small.

Consumers show most movement for brand 1. Although brand 1 shows relatively high reliability (between .5 and .6) in Table 5.6, there is most movement toward and away from it by persons changing their purchase patterns.

Turning from brand loyalty to the projection of brand shares, the various estimates prove less consistent. For each of the four dominant brands—and for brand 10, a new brand on the market—equilibrium brand shares were calculated. These are presented in Table 5.8.

Table 5.8. Equilibrium brand shares for each of five brands, using estimates from four sets of data (using dichotomous calculations).

		Equilibrium brand share p_{i_e}			
	Current Brand		*Purchases skipped*		
Brand	*Share* p_{i_0}	1	2	3	4
1	.136	.127	.164	.180	.174
3	.112	.104	.084	.073	.079
8	.176	.243	.340	.348	.324
9	.185	.083	.074	.150	.163
10	.047	.060	.057	.075	.003

There is some consistency in the predictions: brand 8 is predicted to increase sharply by all sets of data, and brands 3 and 9 are predicted to drop by various amounts. Three of the predictions show an increase in brand 10, but the fourth shows a decline to near zero.

Despite the variations in estimates, however, there are some consistencies, showing declines in certain brands and increases in others. The brand that has most sharply hit the market, 8, is predicted by three of the sets of data to reach a brand share over .30. The projected curves of brand share for this brand, using each of the sets of data, are shown in Fig. 5.12. With one exception these show rather high consistency, not only leading to similar equilibrium points, but also doing so at rather similar rates of speed.

This examination of consumer behavior through data from purchase diary panels is, of course, far from exhaustive. It gives an indication, however, of both the complexities of such analysis and the richness of the information it provides. Much further work needs to be done in improving the estimating procedures, which may allow for more stable estimates with fallible data.

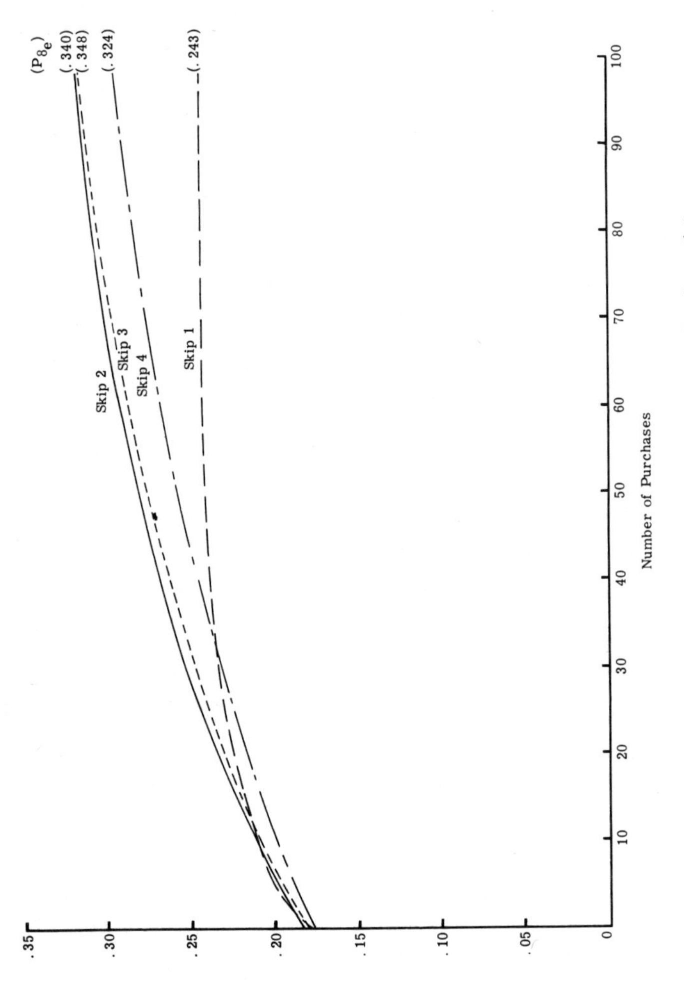

Figure 5.12. Projected brand share, p_{it}, for brand 8.

CHAPTER SIX

Further Directions

It is useful to set down in a separate chapter some of the further directions that proceed from the work carried out here. This may be of use both to those interested in further development of such models and to those interested in the solution of certain research problems.

1. Improved Use of the Present Model

The use that is presently possible with the model is hampered by lack of better estimating procedures. For example, in all but the dichotomous case, it is necessary to estimate separately the Q matrix from pairs of tables, each pair representing three observations. However, it should be possible to carry out calculations that simultaneously use data from a number of waves, and thus to obtain a best fit. For example, one can write from the basic equations of Chap. 2 (using the same matrix notation used in Eq. (2.9) of that chapter):

$$P(0,t) = P(0,0)\ e^{Qt} \tag{1.1}$$

Taking logarithms of both sides and subtracting $ln\ P(0, 0)$ from both sides gives:

$$ln\ P(0, t) - ln\ P(0, 0) = Qt \tag{1.2}$$

Then using the expansion used in Eq. (6.3) of Chap. 2, it appears that one could obtain estimates of the elements of Q and of $P(0, 0)$ by estimating the slope and intercept for each element of the matrix obtained by the expansion of $ln\ P(0, t)$ for various values of t.

In addition to the problem of better estimates is the problem of statistical tests for the model. I have made no progress in this direction; but it is of obvious importance to do so.

2. Heterogeneity in Transition Rates

It was evident in examining certain of the data that in addition to change and response uncertainty, there were differences in transition rates for different persons. I have not been able explicitly to introduce such heterogeneity. It requires some knowledge of, or assumption about, the distribution of individuals according to the size of their transition rates.

One approach in this direction that remains within the present conceptual framework is to weaken the assumption that all persons have the same number of hypothetical elements. If two persons have different numbers of elements, and each element has the same probability of changing, then the individual with more elements will show less radical changes through time. The changes of his elements will tend to cancel each other and give him stability.

It is not clear how to go about introducing such a modification. It will require more data, but in some instances this is no barrier. At present, the main barrier is a conceptual and mathematical one.

A different kind of heterogeneity of transition rates may also be studied. It was assumed above, and has generally been assumed in the literature, that any heterogeneity of transition rates or probabilities must be associated with the individual. This need not be true. There may be classes of events that have a very strong impact, changing many elements, and other classes of events that change only a few. For example, in the case of college plans among high school students, there may be many minor events that happen daily to move the individual closer to one extreme or the other. But along with these mild events come some very strong ones, such as the grades he receives at the end of a school year. Such an event must have a very strong effect, sometimes moving the student from one extreme to the other. Such a conception of a distribution of events in their amounts of impact seems even more difficult to incorporate formally into the model developed here than is heterogeneity among individuals.

3. States Not Directly Related to Response Categories

In all the work above, it was assumed that to each response category there corresponded an underlying state. The elements were associated with states that corresponded directly to the response category.

But this need not be true. It may well be, in a multicategory item (or in a set of categories defined by responses to two or more items), that a given response may depend on the elements in more than one state; and simultaneously, a given state may be connected to more than one response. When such a possibility is conceived, then one can raise a question about the independence of the dimensions in the v-space. It would be possible to examine how much of the variance in position is accounted for by one, two, three, etc., dimensions. In this way one might begin to study multidimensional scaling from a somewhat different direction than has been done before.

Appendix

The computer programs listed below were written in Fortran to carry out on the IBM 7094 all, or nearly all, the computations described in this book. It is evident, of course, that such a program will be outmoded as computer languages develop (particularly those in which matrix operations are carried out directly, without resort to scalar algebra). However, until that time, these programs should be of aid in carrying out calculations described in the text. There are three separate programs, the first of which includes subroutines to carry out a number of distinct operations. The function of each program and subroutine is described by a set of comment cards (with a "C" in column 1) included in the listing of the program. Thus they will be described only briefly here.

1. Program 1: MAIN

This program takes as input two tables that cross tabulate responses between times 0–1 and times 0–2. The time period separating 0 and 1 need not be the same as that separating 1 and 2. When there exist additional waves of data—and additional tables can be constructed for times 0–3, 0–4, etc., and 1–3, 1–4, 2–4, etc.—these data must be analyzed on separate runs, and separate calculations must be carried out for each pair of turnover tables. As calculation methods for estimating Q, $P(0, 0)$, and other parameters from multiwave panels are developed, this program can be modified to gain that additional power.

Program 1 gives as output

1. (INVERT) The elements of the transition matrix $R(t)$ (taking the time period between waves 1 and 2 as the unit of time);
2. (QIJ) Next is calculated the matrix of transition rates Q for the same time period as $R(t)$;
3. (INVERT) The response uncertainties at time 0, $P(0, 0)$, are calculated first from the 0–1 table and then from the 0–2 table;
4. (COVAR) From each of these matrices, $P(0, 0)$, are calculated a covariance matrix for $\text{cov}(v_i, v_j)$, a matrix of values of m_{ij}^*, a matrix of values of c_{ij}, and for each i and j the mean probability of giving response i, given that response i or j is made. The entries of the latter two matrices can be used to calculate, for each two states, the contagious binomial distribution to show the distribution of persons with respect to those states;
5. (RIJ) Using the matrix Q, together with designated times, TT, the transition matrices, $R(TT)$, are calculated for whatever time periods desired. (Note: Because of the construction of the program, when TT becomes large relative to the basic time unit, the calculation will not be correct.)
6. (DICHOT) For arbitrarily selected dichotomizations of the tables, various of the above quantities are calculated, the contagious binomial distribution is calculated, and graphs are printed out giving this distribution together with projections of p_{i_t} and p_{ioi_t}. On the first graph is plotted the contagious binomial and values of p_{ioi_t}/p_{i_t}; on the second is plotted p_{i_t} and p_{ioi_t}. This program also calculates the average individual change, $\Sigma |\Delta v_{it}$ 1.

Since this program is a long and complex one, it may be desirable for some purposes to use the various subroutines as separate programs to calculate particular quantities.

2. Program 2: COHEN

This program takes as input strings of zeros and ones representing sequences of dichotomous responses made by a number of persons. It aggregates over individuals and time and gives estimates of k (or: $q_{01} + q_{10}$). It plots on a graph points such that the slope of the line fitting these points gives an estimate of k. This program was used for analysis of Cohen's data.

3. Program 3 : BAYES

This program takes as input the values of a and c (the probability of giving response 1 in the dichotomous case, and the contagion parameter), and the total number of responses, w, for which *a posteriori* distributions are desired. It prints out a graph for the *a priori* distribution (the contagious binomial) and for each number of positive responses (0, 1, 2, ... w) prints a graph for the *a posteriori* distribution.

Both Program 2 and Program 3 use as subroutines PPLOT and PROP. These two subroutines are listed as part of Program 1.

```
*       XEC
*       LABEL
CMAIN
C       MAIN PRCGRAM FOR CHANGE AND RESPONSE UNCERTAINTY
C       USES SUBROUTINES EQUIL, COVAR, QIJ, RIJ, PROJ, INVERT, DICHOT,
C          PROP, AND PPLOT.  ALSO SYSTEM SUBROUTINES LOGF, EXPF
C       THIS PRCGRAM READS TABLES WITH FORMAT (2X7F10.4), DECIMALS IN 8,18
C          28, ETC.
C       MAXIMUM N IS 16, MAY BE INCREASED BY CHANGING DIMENSION STATEMENTS
C          IN ALL PROGRAMS
C       NPRCB IS INPUT CONSTANT, NUMBER OF SEPARATE PROBLEMS
C       NTM IS INPUT CONSTANT, NUMBER OF TRANSITION MATRICES TO BE MADE
C       T(I) ARE INPUT CONSTANTS, TIME PERIODS OF TRANSITION MATRICES
C           EXPRESSED RELATIVE TO INITIAL TIME SPAN AS UNIT
C       FIRST TWO TIMES GIVE PERIODS FOR TRANSLATING P(I0,J1) TO P(I1,J1)
C           AND P(I0,J2) TO PI2,J2).  FIRST PERIOD IS OBS. 0 TO OBS. 1 AND
C           SECOND IS OBS. 0 TO OBS. 2.  OBS. 1 TO OBS. 2 EQUALS 1.0
C       LAST T, T(NTM), MUST BE 1.0
C       TBL1 AND TBL2 ARE TABLES FOR TIMES 0-1 AND 0-2
        DIMENSICN AT(16,16)
        DIMENSICN NPPL(16)
        DIMENSICN T(30)
        DIMENSICN PC(16)
        DIMENSICN RC(16,16)
        DIMENSICN A (16,16)
        DIMENSICN PT(16,16)
        DIMENSICN ISQ(16,16)
        DIMENSICN R(16,16)
        DIMENSICN P(16,16,2)
        DIMENSICN Q(16,16,2)
        DIMENSICN TBL1(16,16), TBL2(16,16)
        DIMENSICN TS(30)
        DIMENSICN NDI(16)
        DIMENSICN NDIJ(16,16)
        DIMENSICN NRQ(16)
C       READ IN CONSTANTS
        CUT =.0000001
        MM=50
        NTCT=100
        READ INPUT TAPE 5,10,NPROB
        READ INPUT TAPE 5,10,N
        READ INPUT TAPE 5,10,NTM
        READ INPUT TAPE 5,1,(T(I),I=1,NTM)
        M=N+1
        DO 25 I=1,N
        READ INPUT TAPE 5,11, (ISQ(I,J),J=1,N)
    25 CONTINUE
C
C       READ IN SELECTED DICHOTOMIES
C       DATA     READ IN ONCE FOR T12 (TIME BETWEEN OBSERVATIONS 1 AND 2)
C          AND FOR T01 (TIME BETWEEN OBSERVATIONS 0 AND 1).
C       FOR EACH DICHCTOMIZATION  A DATA CARD IS PUNCHED WITH 2-COLUMN
C          NUMBERS, EACH NUMBER BEING A ROW OF MATRIX TO BE LUMPED AS
C          STATE 1.
C       ND IS NUMBER OF DICHOTOMIZATIONS
C       NRW IS NUMBER OF ROWS LUMPED
C       NPPL = NPL = 1 IF TO BE PLOTTED, 0 IF NOT
C       TS(I) IS TIME POINTS FOR PROJECTION
        READ INPUT TAPE 5, 1 ,T12
        READ INPUT TAPE 5, 1 ,T01
```

```
      WRITE OUTPUT TAPE 6,1, TO1,T12
      READ INPUT TAPE 5,10,NT
      READ INPUT TAPE 5,1,(TS(I),I=1,NT)
      WRITE OUTPUT TAPE 6,1, (TS(I),I=1,NT)
      READ INPUT TAPE 5,10,ND
      IF (ND) 165,165,164
  164 CONTINUE
      DO 170 K=1,ND
      READ INPUT TAPE 5,16,NRQ(K),NPPL(K)
      WRITE OUTPUT TAPE 6,98,NRQ(K),NPPL(K)
      NRW=NRQ(K)
      READ INPUT TAPE 5,98,(NDIJ(K,J),J=1,NRW)
      WRITE OUTPUT TAPE 6,98,(NDIJ(K,J),J=1,NRW)
  170 CONTINUE
  165 CONTINUE
      DO 61 NPR=1,NPROB
C
C     READ IN INPUT DATA FOR PROBLEM NN
      DO 126 I=1,N
      READ INPUT TAPE 5,1,(TBL1(I,J),J=1,N)
      TBL1(I,M)=0.
  126 CONTINUE
      DO 127 I=1,N
      READ INPUT TAPE 5,1,(TBL2(I,J),J=1,N)
      TBL2(I,M)=0.
  127 CONTINUE
      TBL1(M,M)=0.
      TBL2(M,M)=0.
      DO 138 J=1,N
      TBL1(M,J)=0.
      TBL2(M,J)=0.
      DO 138 I=1,N
      TEMP1=TBL1(I,J)
      TEMP2=TBL2(I,J)
      TBL1(I,M)=TBL1(I,M) + TEMP1
      TBL2(I,M)=TBL2(I,M) + TEMP2
      TBL1(M,J)=TBL1(M,J) + TEMP1
      TBL2(M,J)=TBL2(M,J) + TEMP2
      TBL1(M,M)=TBL1(M,M) + TEMP1
      TBL2(M,M)=TBL2(M,M) + TEMP2
  138 CONTINUE
      DO 137 I=1,M
      WRITE OUTPUT TAPE 6,15,(TBL1(I,J),J=1,M)
  137 CONTINUE
      DO 136 I=1,M
      WRITE OUTPUT TAPE 6,15,(TBL2(I,J),J=1,M)
  136 CONTINUE
C
      IF (N-2) 185,183,184
  183 CONTINUE
      CALL DICHOT (N,TBL1,TBL2,1,1,NT,TS,T12,TO1,NPL)
      GO TO 61
  184 CONTINUE
C
      WRITE OUTPUT TAPE 6,720, N,CUT,MM,NTOT
  720 FORMAT (1XI3,F10.9,2I5)
      WRITE OUTPUT TAPE 6,721,((ISQ(I,J),J=1,N),I=1,N)
  721 FORMAT (1X121I1)
      DO 135 I=1,M
  135 CONTINUE
```

```
C     CALL SUBROUTINE FOR FINDING Q MATRIX FOR ORIGINAL TABLES
      CALL QIJ (N,TBL1,ISQ,CUT,MM,NTOT,Q,IP,IJ)
      CALL QIJ (N,TBL2,ISQ,CUT,MM,NTOT,Q,IP,IJ)
C
C
C     SET UP TO CALCULATE TRANSITION MATRIX BY SOLVING SIMULT EQNS
C
C     SOLVING FOR R        TBL2 = TBL1*R
C     SOLUTION IS R = TBL1(-1)*TBL2
      CALL INVERT (N,TBL1,A)
C
      DO 105 J=1,M
      R(J,M)=0.
  105 R(M,J)=0.
      DO 107 I=1,N
      DO 107 J=1,N
      R(I,J)=0.
      DO 106 K=1,N
      R(I,J)=R(I,J) + A(I,K)*TBL2(K,J)
  106 CONTINUE
      R(I,M)=R(I,M)+R(I,J)
      R(M,J)=R(M,J)+R(I,J)
      R(M,M)=R(M,M)+R(I,J)
  107 CONTINUE
C
C     WRITE OUT TRANSITION MATRIX
      WRITE OUTPUT TAPE 6,719
      DO 63 I=1,M
      WRITE OUTPUT TAPE 6,718, (R(I,J),J=1,M)
      PUNCH 1, (R(I,J),J=1,M)
   63 CONTINUE
C
C
C     CALL SUBROUTINE FOR FINDING Q MATRIX FOR 3-WAVE PANEL
      CALL QIJ (N,R,ISQ,CUT,MM,NTOT,Q,IP,IJ)
C
      IF(IJ) 61,61,58
   58 CONTINUE
C
C     BEGIN TO REGENERATE TRANSITION PROBABILITIES AND INPUT DATA
      DO 29 IV=1,NTM
      TT=T(IV)
C
      CALL RIJ (N,Q,MM,TT,RC,IP,CUT)
C
C
C     ON FIRST TWO TIMES, CALCULATE AND PRINT OUT UNCERTAINTY AT TIMES 1
C        AND 2 RESPECTIVELY
C
      IF (IV-2) 45,45,43
C
   45 CONTINUE
C     SOLVING FOR UNCERTAINTY
C     SOLVING FOR PT   TBL1 = PT*RC
C     SOLUTION IS PT = TBL1*RC(-1)
      CALL INVERT (N,RC,A)
      WRITE OUTPUT TAPE 6,96, IV,IV
      DO 110 I=1,M
      PT(I,M)=0.
      AT(I,M)=0.
```

```
      PT(M,I)=0.
      AT(M,I)=0.
  110 CONTINUE
      DO 108 I=1,N
      DO 109 J=1,N
      PT(I,J)=0.
      AT(I,J)=0.
      DO 131 K=1,N
      IF (IV-2) 31,32,32
   32 CONTINUE
      PT(I,J)=PT(I,J) + TBL2(I,K)*A(K,J)/TBL2(M,M)
      AT(I,J)=AT(I,J) + TBL2(I,K)*A(K,J)/ (TBL2(I,M)*TBL2(J,M))**.5
      GO TO 131
   31 CONTINUE
      PT(I,J)=PT(I,J) + TBL1(I,K)*A(K,J)/TBL1(M,M)
      AT(I,J)=AT(I,J) + TBL1(I,K)*A(K,J)/ (TBL1(I,M)*TBL1(J,M))**.5
  131 CONTINUE
      PT(I,M)=PT(I,M)+PT(I,J)
      PT(M,J)=PT(M,J)+PT(I,J)
      PT(M,M)=PT(M,M)+PT(I,J)
      AT(I,M)=AT(I,M)+AT(I,J)
      AT(M,J)=AT(M,J)+AT(I,J)
      AT(M,M)=AT(M,M)+AT(I,J)
  109 CONTINUE
  108 CONTINUE
      DO 102 I=1,M
      WRITE OUTPUT TAPE 6,15,(PT(I,J),J=1,M)
  102 CONTINUE
      WRITE OUTPUT TAPE 6,18
      DO 181 I=1,M
      WRITE OUTPUT TAPE 6,15,(AT(I,J),J=1,M)
  181 CONTINUE
C     CALL SUBROUTINE TO FIND COVARIANCES AND OTHER MEASURES
      CALL COVAR (N,PT,A)
   43 CONTINUE
   29 CONTINUE
      IF (ND) 167,167,166
  166 CONTINUE
      DO 169 I=1,ND
      NRW=NRC(I)
      NPL=NPPL(K)
      DO 168 J=1,NRW
      NDI(J)=NDIJ(I,J)
  168 CONTINUE
      CALL DICHOT (N,TBL1,TBL2,NRW,NDI,NT,TS,T12,T01,NPL)
  169 CONTINUE
  167 CONTINUE
C
C     OUTPUT REGENERATED DATA
      CALL PROJ (N,RC,R)
C     OUTPUT INPUT DATA
      WRITE OUTPUT TAPE 6, 8, (I,I=1,N)
      DO 33 I=1,M
      WRITE OUTPUT TAPE 6,5,  I,(R (I,J),J=1,M)
   33 CONTINUE
   61 CONTINUE
  185 CONTINUE
      CALL EXIT
    1 FORMAT (2X7F10.4)
    2 FORMAT (I4,3X,16F7.3)
```

```
    3 FORMAT (5A6)
    4 FORMAT (F9.8,3X,2I4)
    5 FORMAT (I4,(1X,16F8.4))
    6 FORMAT (8X(7F8.0))
    7 FORMAT (// 1X,11HCALC P, N ,/(I4,16I8))
    8 FORMAT (// 11H ACT N(I,J) ,/(I4,16I8))
    9 FORMAT (5XI3, 20H  CYCLES NOT ENOUGH    )
   10 FORMAT (I2)
   11 FORMAT (30I1)
   12 FORMAT (16(I6,I1),7X)
   13 FORMAT (3XI4,(16F7.3))
   14 FORMAT (7H1Q(I,J) )
   15 FORMAT (2X16F8.4)
   16 FORMAT (36I2)
   17 FORMAT (/)
   18 FORMAT (28H  P(IO,JO)/(P(IO)*P(JO)**.5)   )
   91 FORMAT (I4,(3X,12F10.4))
   92 FORMAT (25H NUMBER OF TERMS FOR I =  ,I2,4H IS , I2)
   93 FORMAT (I4,(3X,12F10.4))
   94 FORMAT (/7H TIME = ,F10.4)
   95 FORMAT (12F6.0)
   96 FORMAT (/1X 21HP(IO,JO) USING P(IO,J ,I1,1H),19H AND RC FOR TIME 0
     1-   ,I1)
   97 FORMAT (7X12F10.4)
   98 FORMAT(2X35I2)
  718 FORMAT (2X7F10.7)
  719 FORMAT (1X 6HR(I,J))
      END
      SUBROUTINE COVAR (N,PT,A)
*     LABEL
CCOVAR
C     THIS SUBROUTINE CALCULATES COVARIANCES ACROSS PEOPLE, MEASURES OF
C        UNCERTAINTY M* AND C FOR ALL CELLS, AND RELATIVE MARGINALS FOR
C        ALL CELLS.
C     COVARIANCES ARE P(IT,JT) - P(IT)*P(JT)
C     M* IS NUMBER OF INDEPENDENT ELEMENTS IN RESPONSE.
C     M*(I,I)=P(IT)*(1.-P(IT))/(P(IT,IT) - P(IT)*P(IT))
C        M*(I,J)=P(IT)*P(JT)/(P(IT)*P(JT) - P(IT,JT))
C     RELATIVE MARGINALS ARE  P(I/J)=P(IT)/(P(IT)+P(JT))
C     POLARIZATION OR CONTAGION IS C(I,J)=1./(M*(I,J) - 1.)
C
      DIMENSION PT(16,16)
      DIMENSION A (16,16)
      M=N+1
C
C     OBTAIN COVARIANCES
      DO 19 J=1,M
      A(M,J)=0.
   19 CONTINUE
      DO 20 I=1,N
      A(I,M)=0.
      DO 20 J=1,N
      A(I,J)=PT(I,J)/PT(M,M) - PT(I,M)*PT(J,M)/(PT(M,M)*PT(M,M))
      A(I,M)=A(I,M)+A(I,J)
      A(M,J)=A(M,J)+A(I,J)
      A(M,M)=A(M,M)+A(I,J)
   20 CONTINUE
      WRITE OUTPUT TAPE 6,161
      DO 21 I=1,M
      WRITE OUTPUT TAPE 6,160,I,(A(I,J),J=1,M)
```

```
   21 CONTINUE
C
C      OBTAIN M*
       DO 22 J=1,M
       A(M,J)=0.
   22 CONTINUE
       DO 23 I=1,N
       A(I,M)=0.
       DO 23 J=1,N
       IF (I-J) 24,25,24
   24 CONTINUE
       A(I,J)=PT(I,M)*PT(J,M)/(-A(I,J)*PT(M,M)*PT(M,M))
       GO TO 26
   25 CONTINUE
       A(I,J)=(PT(I,M)/PT(M,M))*(1.-PT(I,M)/PT(M,M))/A(I,J)
   26 CONTINUE
       A(I,M)=A(I,M)+A(I,J)
       A(M,J)=A(M,J)+A(I,J)
       A(M,M)=A(M,M)+A(I,J)
   23 CONTINUE
       WRITE OUTPUT TAPE 6,162
       DO 27 I=1,M
       WRITE OUTPUT TAPE 6,160,I,(A(I,J),J=1,M)
   27 CONTINUE
C
C      OBTAIN POLARIZATION C
       DO 28 J=1,M
       A(M,J)=0.
   28 CONTINUE
       DO 29 I=1,N
       A(I,M)=0.
       DO 29 J=1,N
       A(I,J)=1./(A(I,J)-1.)
       A(I,M)=A(I,M)+A(I,J)
       A(M,J)=A(M,J)+A(I,J)
       A(M,M)=A(M,M)+A(I,J)
   29 CONTINUE
       WRITE OUTPUT TAPE 6,163
       DO 30 I=1,M
       WRITE OUTPUT TAPE 6,160,I,(A(I,J),J=1,M)
   30 CONTINUE
C
C      OBTAIN RELATIVE MARGINALS
       DO 31 J=1,M
       A(M,J)=0.
   31 CONTINUE
       DO 32 I=1,N
       A(I,M)=0.
       DO 32 J=1,N
       A(I,J)=PT(I,M)/(PT(I,M)+PT(J,M))
       A(I,M)=A(I,M)+A(I,J)
       A(M,J)=A(M,J)+A(I,J)
       A(M,M)=A(M,M)+A(I,J)
   32 CONTINUE
       WRITE OUTPUT TAPE 6,164
       DO 33 I=1,M
       WRITE OUTPUT TAPE 6,160,I,(A(I,J),J=1,M)
   33 CONTINUE
       RETURN
  160 FORMAT (1XI3,16(1XF7.3))
```

```
  161 FORMAT (/1X22HCOVARIANCES COV(VI,VJ))
  162 FORMAT (/1X51HM*(I,J), NUMBER OF INDEPENDENT ELEMENTS IN RESPONSE)
  163 FORMAT (/1X40HC(I,J), CONTAGION PARAMETER FOR ELEMENTS)
  164 FORMAT (/1X29HRELATIVE MARGINALS PR(I/IORJ))
      END
      SUBROUTINE QIJ (N,R,ISQ,CUT,MM,NTOT,Q,IP,IJ)
*     LABEL
CQIJ
C     SOLVES FOR QIJS SUBJECT TO CONSTRAINTS IMPOSED BY ISQ
C     CALLING SEQUENCE IS
C     CALL QIJ (N,R,ISQ,CUT,MM,NTOT,Q,IP,IJ)
C     N IS INPUT CONSTANT, SIZE OF MATRIX
C     R(I,J) IS INPUT TABLE OF DATA WITH ROW AND COLUMN SUMS
C     ISQ(I,J) IS MATRIX OF ZEROES AND ONES, ONES ONLY WHERE WHERE
C         POSITIVE Q(I,J)S ARE DESIRED
C     CUT IS INPUT CONSTANT FOR SIZE OF LAST TERM IN SERIES E.G. .00001
C     MM IS INPUT CONSTANT, MAXIMUM NUMBER OF TERMS IN EACH ITERATION
C     NTOT IS INPUT CONSTANT, MAXIMUM NUMBER OF ITERATION CYCLES FOR QIJ
C     OUTPUT IS Q(I,J)S IF ITERATION CONVERGES
C     IP IS 1 OR 2 DEPENDING ON LOCATION OF LAST ITERATION OF Q(I,J)S
C     IJ IS 0 IF ITERATION DOES NOT CONVERGE, 1 IF ITERATION CONVERGES
      DIMENSION ISQ(16,16)
      DIMENSION R(16,16)
      DIMENSION Q(16,16,2)
      DIMENSION P(16,16,2)
      M=N+1
      CTT =400.*CUT
      IP=1
      IT=2
C     SET UP INITIAL VALUES FOR Q(I,J)
      DO 21 I=1,N
      Q(I,I,IP)=0.
      DO 21 J=1,N
      IF (I-J) 20,21,20
   20 CONTINUE
      IF (ISQ(I,J)) 22,24,22
   24 CONTINUE
      Q(I,J,IP)=0.
      GO TO 21
   22 CONTINUE
      Q(I,J,IP) =R(I,J)/R(I,M)
      Q(I,I,IP) =Q(I,I,IP)-Q(I,J,IP)
   21 CONTINUE
      WRITE OUTPUT TAPE 6,14
      DO 27 I=1,N
      WRITE OUTPUT TAPE6,12, ((I,J),J=1,N)
   27 CONTINUE
C
C     GO INTO ITERATION CYCLES
      DO 44 NCY=1,NTOT
      DO 51 I=1,N
      IA=1
      IB=2
      DO 82 J=1,N
      Q(I,J,IT) =R(I,J)/R(I,M)
      P(I,J,IB) =Q(I,J,IP)
   82 CONTINUE
C
C     START LOOP WHICH ADDS A TERM TO SERIES ON EACH CYCLE
      DO 83 L=2,MM
```

```
      FL=L
      DO 85 J=1,N
      P(I,J,IA)=0.
      DO 86 K=1,N
      P(I,J,IA) =P(I,J,IA) + P(I,K,IB)*Q(K,J,IP)/FL
   86 CONTINUE
      Q(I,J,IT) =Q(I,J,IT) - P(I,J,IA)
   85 CONTINUE
      ITEMP =IB
      IB=IA
      IA=ITEMP
      DO 87 J=1,N
      TEMP =P(I,J,IB)*P(I,J,IB)
      IF (TEMP-CUT) 87,83,83
   87 CONTINUE
      GO TO 89
   83 CONTINUE
C
C     EXIT FROM SERIES IF NO CONVERGENCE
      WRITE OUTPUT TAPE 6,9,L
      IJ=0
      GO TO 59
   89 CONTINUE
      DO 52 J=1,N
      IF (I-J) 50,53,50
   50 CONTINUE
      IF (ISQ(I,J)) 52,53,52
   53 CONTINUE
      Q(I,J,IT)=0.
   52 CONTINUE
   51 CONTINUE
      DO 31 I=1,N
      Q(I,I,IT)=0.
      DO 31 J=1,N
      IF(I-J) 32,31,32
   32 Q(I,I,IT) = Q(I,I,IT) - Q(I,J,IT)
   31 CONTINUE
      ITEMP =IT
      IT=IP
      IP=ITEMP
      DO 41 I=1,N
      DO 41 J=1,N
      TEMP = (Q(I,J,IT) - Q(I,J,IP))**2
      IF (TEMP-CTT) 41,44,44
   41 CONTINUE
      DO 28 I=1,N
      WRITE OUTPUT TAPE 6,13,NCY, (Q(I,J,IP),J=1,N)
   28 CONTINUE
      GO TO 60
   44 CONTINUE
C
C     EXIT FROM ITERATION IF ITERATION FAILS TO CONVERGE
      DO 128 I = 1,N
      WRITE OUTPUT TAPE 6,13,NCY, (Q(I,J,IT), J = 1,N)
      WRITE OUTPUT TAPE 6,13,NCY, (Q(I,J,IP), J = 1,N)
  128 CONTINUE
      IJ=0
      GO TO 59
   60 CONTINUE
      IJ=1
```

```
   59 CONTINUE
    9 FORMAT (5XI3, 20H  CYCLES NOT ENOUGH    )
   12 FORMAT (16(I6,I1),7X)
   13 FORMAT (3XI4,(16F7.3))
   14 FORMAT (7H1Q(I,J) )
      RETURN
      END
      SUBROUTINE RIJ (N,Q,MM,TT,RC,IP,CUT)
*     LABEL
CRIJ
C     CALCULATES TRANSITION MATRIX FOR TIME TT, GIVEN RATES QIJ
C     CALLING SEQUENCE IS
C     CALL RIJ (N,Q,MM,TT,RC,IP,CUT)
C     N IS NUMBER OF ROWS AND COLUMNS IN MATRIX
C     Q IS 3 DIMENSIONAL ARRAY NXNX2 CONTAINING Q(I,J)S
C     MM IS MAXIMUM NUMBER OF TERMS IN EACH SERIES
C     TT IS TIME PERIOD OF TRANSITION MATRIX RELATIVE TO PERIOD FOR QIJS
C     RC IS OUTPUT MATRIX OF TRANSITION PROBABILITIES
C     IP IS LOCATION OF FINAL QIJS IN MATRIX (=1 OR 2)
C     CUT IS INPUT CONSTANT FOR SIZE OF LAST TERM IN SERIES
      DIMENSION RC(16,16)
      DIMENSION Q(16,16,2)
      DIMENSION P(16,16,2)
      M=N+1
      IA=1
      IB=2
      DO 79 I=1,N
      DO 79 J=1,N
      P(I,J,IB)=0.
      RC(I,J   )=0.
   79 CONTINUE
      DO 77 I=1,N
      IA=1
      IB=2
      P(I,I,IB)=1.
      RC(I,I   )=1.
      RC(I,M   )=1.
      DO 75 L=1,MM
      FL=L
      DO 74 J=1,N
      P(I,J,IA)=0.
      DO 71 K=1,N
      P(I,J,IA)= P(I,J,IA) + P(I,K,IB)*Q(K,J,IP)*TT/FL
   71 CONTINUE
      RC(I,J   )=RC(I,J   ) + P(I,J,IA)
   74 CONTINUE
      ITEMP=IB
      IB=IA
      IA=ITEMP
      DO 81 J=1,N
      TEMP = P(I,J,IB)*P(I,J,IB)
      IF (TEMP-CUT) 81,84,84
   81 CONTINUE
      WRITE OUTPUT TAPE 6,92,I,L
      GO TO 77
   84 CONTINUE
   75 CONTINUE
      LM=L-1
      WRITE OUTPUT TAPE 6,9,LM
   77 CONTINUE
```

```
      DO 68 J=1,M
      RC(M,J   )=0.
      DO 68 I=1,N
      RC(M,J   )=RC(M,J   ) + RC(I,J   )
   68 CONTINUE
C
C     OUTPUT TRANSITION PROBABILITIES
      WRITE OUTPUT TAPE 6,94,TT
      DO 39 I=1,M
      WRITE OUTPUT TAPE 6,91,       I,(RC(I,J   ),J=1,M)
   39 CONTINUE
    1 FORMAT (2X7F10.4)
    9 FORMAT (5XI3, 20H  TERMS  NOT ENOUGH    )
   91 FORMAT (I4,(3X,12F10.4))
   92 FORMAT (25H NUMBER OF TERMS FOR I =  ,I2,4H IS , I2)
   94 FORMAT (/7H TIME = ,F10.4)
      RETURN
      END
      SUBROUTINE PROJ (N,RC,R)
*     LABEL
CPROJ
C     PRCJECTS FOR ONE TIME PERIOD, GIVEN TRANSITION MATRIX RC AND VECT
C        CR R
C     CALLING SEQUENCE IS
C     CALL PRCJ(N,RC,R)
C     N IS SIZE OF TRANSITION MATRIX
C     R(I,M) IS INPUT MARGINALS AT TIME 0
C     RC(I,J) IS CALCULATED TRANSITION TABLE FROM TIME 0 TO T, WITH
C        R(M,J) AS VECTOR OF STATES AT TIME T
      DIMENSICN RC(16,16)
      DIMENSICN R(16,16)
      M=N+1
      DO 67 I=1,N
      RC(I,M   )=R(I,M)
      DO 67 J=1,N
      RC(I,J   )=RC(I,J   )*R(I,M)
   67 CONTINUE
      DC 63 I=1,N
      RC(I,M   )=R(I,M)
   63 CONTINUE
      DC 65 J=1,M
      RC(M,J   )=0.
      DO 65 I=1,N
      RC(M,J   ) = RC(M,J   ) + RC(I,J   )
   65 CONTINUE
      DO 30 I=1,M
      WRITE OUTPUT TAPE 6,93,       I,(RC(I,J   ),J=1,M)
   30 CONTINUE
   93 FORMAT (I4,(1X,16F8.4))
C
      RETURN
      END
      SUBROUTINE INVERT (N,X,XI)
*     LABEL
CINVERT
C     INVERTS AN NXN MATRIX
C     X IS INPUT MATRIX, N*N
C     XI IS OUTPUT MATRIX, INVERSE OF X
      DIMENSION X(16,16)
      DIMENSION XI(16,16)
```

```
      DIMENSION A (16,16)
      DO 201 JJ=1,N
      DO 202 I=1,N
      A(I,N+1)=0.
      DO 202 J=1,N
      A(I,J)=X(I,J)
  202 CONTINUE
      A(JJ,N+1)=1.
      NTT =N
      NTTM =N-1
      NTTP =N+1
      DO 91 I=1,NTTM
      IPL = I+1
      DO 91 J=IPL,NTT
      IF (A(I,I)) 86,87,86
   86 BJI= A(J,I)/A(I,I)
      DO 91 K=I,NTTP
      A(J,K)= A(J,K) - A(I,K)*BJI
   91 CONTINUE
      XI(NTT,JJ) =A(NTT,NTTP)/A(NTT,NTT)
C
C     REPLACE VARIABLES ONE BY ONE TO SOLVE FOR OTHER N-1 R(I,J)S
      DO 84 J=1,NTTM
      TEMP=0.
      DO 83 I=1,J
      K=I-1
      NTTJ=NTT-J
      NTTK=NTT-K
   83 TEMP=TEMP + A(NTTJ,NTTK)*XI(NTTK,JJ)
      XI(NTTJ,JJ) = (A(NTTJ,NTTP) - TEMP)/A(NTTJ,NTTJ)
   84 CONTINUE
   88 CONTINUE
  201 CONTINUE
      RETURN
   87 CONTINUE
      WRITE OUTPUT TAPE 6,722
      GO TO 88
  722 FORMAT (1X19HDENOMINATOR IS ZERO )
      END
      SUBROUTINE DICHOT (N,TBL1,TBL2,NRW,NDI,NTM,T,AVDAYS,AVD1,NPL)
*     LABEL
CDICHOT
C     CALCULATES FOR SELECTED DICHOTOMIES
C     THIS SUBROUTINE USES PROP AND PPLOT AS SUBROUTINES
C     CALLING SEQUENCE IS
C     CALL       DICHOT (N,TBL1,TBL2,NRW,NDI,NTM,T,AVDAYS,AVD1,NPL)
C     N IS SIZE OF TABLES
C      OUTPUT IS EQUILIBRIUM P, POLARIZATION C, MOVEMENT K, PROJECTION
C        FOR GIVEN TIMES T(1) THROUGH T(NTM), AND AVERAGE MOVEMENT OF
C     INDIVIDUAL.  ALSO DISTRIBUTION OF INDIVIDUALS IS GRAPHED, AS IS P1
C     AND P11 AT TIMES T(1) THROUGH T(NTM).
C     THIS SUBROUTINE USES PROP AND PPLOT AS SUBROUTINES.
      DIMENSION NDI(16)
      DIMENSION TBL1(16,16), TBL2(16,16)
      DIMENSION T(30)
      DIMENSION PX(30), PXXT(30)
      DIMENSION X(101)
      DIMENSION  PP(101)
      DIMENSION P11T(101), P1(101), PV(101)
      M=N+1
```

```
      P10=0.
      P11=0.
      P12=0.
      P111=0.
      P112=0.
      DO 171 L=1,NRW
      I=NDI(L)
      P10=P10+TBL1(I,M)
      P11=P11+TBL1(M,I)
      P12=P12+TBL2(M,I)
      DO 171 LL=1,NRW
      J=NDI(LL)
      P111=P111+TBL1(I,J)
      P112=P112+TBL2(I,J)
  171 CONTINUE
      TEMP1=TBL1(M,M)
      TEMP2=TBL2(M,M)
      P10=P10/TEMP1
      P11=P11/TEMP1
      P12=P12/TEMP2
      P111=P111/TEMP1
      P112=P112/TEMP2
      DO 73 I=1,101
      X(I)=I-1
      PV(I)=0.
      P1(I) =0.
      P11T(I) =0.
   73 CONTINUE
      DEC1=0.
      NP=101
      XPON1=(P112-P12*P10)/(P111-P11*P10)
      TK= -LOGF(XPON1)/AVDAYS
      QT= -AVD1*TK
      XPONA= EXPF(QT)
      P1E= (P111*P12 - P112*P11)/(P111 - P112 + P10*(P12-P11))
      TMPA= 1. + 1./XPONA + 1./XPONA*XPON1
      TMPA=TMPA*P1E
      TMPB =P10 + P11/XPONA + P12/XPONA*XPON1
      P1CC= P1E +    ((TMPB - TMPA)/3.)
      P11C= P1E +    ((TMPB - TMPA)/3.)*XPONA
      P12C= P1E +    ((TMPB - TMPA)/3.)*XPONA*XPON1
      TEMP5=(P111 - P11*P10)/XPONA
      TEMP6=(P112 - P12*P10)/(XPONA*XPON1)
      TEMP7 =.5*(TEMP5 + TEMP6)
      P11CC= P10*P10 + TEMP7
      P111C= P11*P10 + TEMP7*XPONA
      P112C= P12*P10 + TEMP7*XPONA*XPON1
      DO 71 L=1,NTM
      TIME = T(L)/AVDAYS
      I=T(L)+1.
      TEMP9=XPON1**TIME
      P1(I)= P1E + ((TMPB-TMPA)/3.)*TEMP9
      P11T(I)=P10*P1(I) + TEMP9*TEMP7
      PV(I)   =P11T(I)/P1(I)
      PX(L)=P1(I)
      PXXT(L)=P11T(I)
   71 CONTINUE
      C=(P11CC - P10*P10)/(P10 - P11OC)
      WRITE OUTPUT TAPE 6,707,L
      WRITE OUTPUT TAPE 6,702, (T(I),I=1,NTM)
```

```
      WRITE OUTPUT TAPE 6,705, (PX(I),I=1,NTM)
      WRITE OUTPUT TAPE 6,705, (PXXT(I),I=1,NTM)
      WRITE OUTPUT TAPE 6,706,  P1E, TK,C
      WRITE OUTPUT TAPE 6,777,  P10,P11,P12,P111,P112,P10C,P11C,P12C,
     1P110C,P111C,P112C
      CALL PRCP(P10,C,NP,PP,DEC1)
C     CALCULATE EXPECTED CHANGE AT LEVEL OF INDIVIDUAL.
C     TIME PERIOD IS IN UNITS EQUAL TO TIME BETWEEN 2ND AND 3RD OBSERV.
      DVP=0.
      DVN=0.
      TX=NP-1
      DO 193 I=1,NP
      TP=I-1
      TP=TP/TX
      TEMP=(P10-TP)*PP(I)
      IF (TEMP) 191,191,192
  191 DVN=DVN+TK*TEMP
      GO TO 193
  192 DVP=DVP+TK*TEMP
  193 CONTINUE
      DELTV=DVP-DVN
      WRITE OUTPUT TAPE 6,740, DVP,DVN,DELTV
      IF (NPL) 194,194,195
  195 CONTINUE
C   CALLING SEQUENCE IS
C     CALL PPLOT(NSP,X1,Y1,X2,Y2,K,Y1MAX,Y1MIN,Y2MAX,Y2MIN)
C       NSP=NO. OF SAMPLE POINTS
C     X1= FIRST X-ARRAY
C    Y1= FIRST DEPENDENT ARRAY
C   X2= SECOND X-ARRAY
C    Y2=SECOND DEPENDENT ARRAY
C    K=1 FOR COMMON SCALES
C      =C FOR INDEPENDENT SCALES
C    YMAX=MAX VALUE OF Y1
C    Y1MIN=MIN VALUE OF Y1
C   Y2MAX=MAX VALUE OF Y2
C     Y2MIN = MIN VALUE OF Y2
C     IF MAX AND MIN ARE EQUAL, THEN SCALING IS AUTOMATICALLY DONE FOR
C         MAXIMUM DISPLAY
      NX=T(NTM)
      CALL PPLOT (NP,X,PP,X,PV,0,.1,0.,0.,0.)
      CALL PPLOT  (NX,X,P11T,X,P1,1,0.,0.,0.,0.)
  194 CONTINUE
      RETURN
  702 FORMAT (/ 1X21H       DAYS IN FUTURE /      (8X17F7.0))
  705 FORMAT (/9X17F7.4)
  706 FORMAT (/1X16HEQUILIBRIUM P =   ,F7.4, 15HMOVEMENT (K) =   ,F7.4,
     1  18HPOLARIZATION (C) =   ,F7.4)
  707 FORMAT (/// 1X14HPROJECTION NO. ,I5)
  777 FORMAT(/14X62HP10     P11     P12     P110    P111    P112         ,
     1            /1X6HACTUAL,5X3F7.4,7X2F7.4,       /,1X10HCALCULATED,1X
     26F7.4)
  740 FORMAT (/1X 29HAV. INDIV. CHANGE POSITIVE = ,F7.4,11HNEGATIVE = ,
     1F7.4, 8HTOTAL = ,F7.4 /)
      END
      SUBROUTINE PPLOT(NX,XA,A,XB,B,K,AMAX,AMIN,BMAX,BMIN)
*     LABEL
CPPLOT
C   CALLING SEQUENCE IS
C     CALL PPLOT(NSP,X1,Y1,X2,Y2,K,Y1MAX,Y1MIN,Y2MAX,Y2MIN)
```

```
C          NSP=NO. OF SAMPLE POINTS
C        X1= FIRST X-ARRAY
C      Y1= FIRST DEPENDENT ARRAY
C    X2= SECOND X-ARRAY
C      Y2=SECOND DEPENDENT ARRAY
C      K=1 FOR COMMON SCALES
C         =0 FOR INDEPENDENT SCALES
C      YMAX=MAX VALUE OF Y1
C      Y1MIN=MIN VALUE OF Y1
C    Y2MAX=MAX VALUE OF Y2
C        Y2MIN = MIN VALUE OF Y2
C        IF MAX AND MIN ARE EQUAL, THEN SCALING IS AUTOMATICALLY DNOE FOR
C              MAXIMUM DISPLAY
        DIMENSION WRITE(21),WRD(3),WORD(3),ALL(3),A(101),B(101),XA(101),
      1XB(101),ASIDE(11),BSIDE(11),ELIM(5)
        XEKF(C,SC,CMN)=(C-CMN)*SC+.001
        XLKF(C,SC,CMN)=XMODF((202+XSIGNF(1,XEKF(C,SC,CMN)))/2
      1+XEKF(C,SC,CMN)-((XEKF(C,SC,CMN)-XSIGNF(1,XEKF(C,SC,CMN)))/100)
      2*100,101)
        XBLKF(C,SC,CMN)=XLKF(C,SC,CMN)/5+1
        XACCF(C,SC,CMN)=XMODF(XLKF(C,SC,CMN),5)+1
B       RICDF(A,B,C)=A*B+C*(-B)
B       SCALE=204040404040
B       ASTRIK=545454545454
B       DOT=333333333333
B       BLANK=606060606060
B       WRD(1)=BLANK
B       WRD(2)=BLANK
B       WRD(3)=SCALE
B       WORD(1)=316060606060
B       WORD(2)=206060606060
B       WORD(3)=SCALE
B       ALL(1)=313131313131
B       ALL(2)=ALL(1)
B       ALL(3)=202020202020
B       ELIM(1)=007777777777
B       ELIM(2)=770077777777
B       ELIM(3)=777700777777
B       ELIM(4)=777777007777
B       ELIM(5)=777777770077
        KA=1
        KB=1
        AMX=A(1)
        AMN=A(1)
        BMN=B(1)
        BMX=B(1)
        DO8I=1,NX
        AMX=MAX1F(AMX,A(I))
        AMN=MIN1F(AMN,A(I))
        BMN=MIN1F(BMN,B(I))
      8 BMX=MAX1F(BMX,B(I))
        IF(AMX-AMN)9,9,10
      9 AMX=AMX+.4*(ABSF(AMX)+1.0)
        AMN=AMN-.6*(ABSF(AMN)+1.0)
        KA=2
     10 IF(BMX-BMN)11,11,12
     11 BMX=BMX+.6*(ABSF(BMX)+1.0)
        BMN=BMN-.4*(ABSF(BMN)+1.0)
        KB=2
     12 GO TO (13,15),KA
```

```
   13 IF(AMAX-AMIN) 15,15,14
   14 AMN=AMIN
      AMX=AMAX
   15 GO TO (16,18),KB
   16 IF(BMAX-BMIN) 18,18,17
   17 BMN=BMIN
      BMX=BMAX
   18 IF(K) 20,20,19
   19 BMX=MAX1F(AMX,BMX)
      AMX=BMX
      BMN=MIN1F(AMN,BMN)
      AMN=BMN
   20 SA=100.01/(AMX-AMN)
      SB=100.01/(BMX-BMN)
      MA=LOGF(MAX1F(ABSF(AMN),ABSF(AMX)))/LOGF(10.0)
      MB=LOGF(MAX1F(ABSF(BMN),ABSF(BMX)))/LOGF(10.0)
      A10=(AMX-AMN)*10.0**(-MA-1)
      B10=(BMX-BMN)*10.0**(-MB-1)
      ASIDE(1)=AMN*10.0**(-MA)
      BSIDE(1)=BMN*10.0**(-MB)
      DO 23 J=1,10
      ASIDE(J+1)= ASIDE(J)+A10
   23 BSIDE(J+1)= BSIDE(J)+B10
      IF(K) 200,200,204
  200 IZERO=2
      ALL(1)=WORD(1)
      ALL(2)=WORD(2)
      GO TO 30
  204 IF(BMX) 200,200,205
  205 IF(BMN) 206,200,200
  206 IZERO=XBLKF(0.0,SA,AMN)
      IZAC=XACCF(0.0,SA,AMN)
      IF(IZAC-1+(IZERO-1)*(21-IZERO)) 200,200,216
  216 DO 207 MM=1,3
      WRITE(IZERO)=WRD(MM)
      WRITE(1)=WORD(MM)
      WRITE(21)=WORD(MM)
B     WRD(MM)=RIDDF(WRITE(IZERO),ELIM(IZAC),ALL(MM))
      WORD(MM)=WRITE(1)
  207 ALL(MM)=WRITE(21)
   30 WRITE OUTPUT TAPE 6,500,MA
   32 WRITE OUTPUT TAPE 6,502,ASIDE
   31 DO 43 KK=1,NX
      IF(KK-1) 301,301,303
  303 IF(KK-NX) 304,301,301
  304  GO TO (305,307),IFINK
  301 DO 302 MM=1,21
  302 WRITE(MM)=SCALE
      IFINK=1
      WRITE(IZERO)=WRD(3)
      GO TO 35
  305 DO 306 MM=1,21
  306 WRITE(MM)=BLANK
      IFINK=2
  307 IF(XMODF(KK-1,5)) 308,308,309
  308 WRITE(1)=WORD(2)
      WRITE(21)=ALL(2)
      WRITE(IZERO)=WRD(2)
      GO TO 35
  309 WRITE(1)=WORD(1)
```

```
      WRITE(21)=ALL(1)
      WRITE(IZERO)=WRD(1)
   35 IBBLK=XBLKF(B(KK),SB,BMN)
      IBACC=XACCF(B(KK),SB,BMN)
B     WRITE(IBBLK)=RIDDF(WRITE(IBBLK),ELIM(IBACC),DOT)
      IABLK=XBLKF(A(KK),SA,AMN)
      IAACC=XACCF(A(KK),SA,AMN)
B     WRITE(IABLK)=RIDDF(WRITE(IABLK),ELIM(IAACC),ASTRIK)
      IF(XMODF(KK-1,5))  40,40,41
   40 WRITE OUTPUT TAPE 6,504,XA(KK),WRITE,XB(KK)
      GO TO 42
   41 WRITE OUTPUT TAPE 6,505,WRITE
   42 WRITE(IBBLK)=BLANK
   43 WRITE(IABLK)=BLANK
      WRITE OUTPUT TAPE 6,502,BSIDE
      WRITE OUTPUT TAPE 6,501,MB
  500 FORMAT(1H+,83X,18H(MULTIPLY BY 10**(,I3,2H)))
  501 FORMAT(84X,18H(MULTIPLY BY 10**(,I3,2H)))
  502 FORMAT(9X3H(*)F9.2,10F10.2,5X3H(.))
  504 FORMAT(8X,1PE10.2,20A5,A1,1PE9.2)
  505 FORMAT(18X,20A5,A1)
      RETURN
      END
      SUBROUTINE PROP(A,C,M,FNC,DEC1)
*     LABEL
CPROP
      DIMENSION FNC(1001)
      NTP1=5
      NTP2=6
      FMT=M-1
      FNC(1)=1.-A
      FI=1.
      DO 120 I=3,M
      FNC(1)=FNC(1)*(1.-A+FI*C)/(1.+FI*C)
 120  FI=FI+1.
      FI=0.
      SUM=FNC(1)
      DO 200 I=2,M
      FNC(I)=FNC(I-1)*(FMT-FI)/(FI+1.)*(A+FI*C)/(1.-A+(FMT-FI-1.)*C)
      FI=FI+1.
 200  SUM=SUM+FNC(I)
      WRITE OUTPUT TAPE NTP2,2,(I,FNC(I),I=1,M)
    2 FORMAT(6(I5,F10.6))
      IF(DEC1)6,5,6
    6 ZERM=0
      FIRM=0
      SECM=0
      DO 100 I=1,M
      ZERM=ZERM+FNC(I)
      FJ=I-1
      FIRM=FIRM+FJ*FNC(I)
  100 SECM=SECM+FJ*FJ*FNC(I)
      AVE=FIRM/ZERM
      VAR=SECM/ZERM-AVE*AVE
      WRITE OUTPUT TAPE NTP2,4,FIRM,AVE,VAR
    4 FORMAT(5F15.6)
      WRITE OUTPUT TAPE NTP2,3,A,C,M,SUM
    3 FORMAT(2F10.4,I10,F15.6)
    5 RETURN
      END
```

```
*      DATA
 1    NPROB
 4    N
 5    NTM
        .3333     1.3333      .5         1.5         1.          T(I)
0110
1001
1001
0110
       1.          AVDAYS
        .3333      AVD1
 5    NT
        .          .333      1.0         1.5         5.          T(I)
 2  ND
 2 1  NRW  NPL
   1 2      NCI
 2 1  NRW  NPL
   1 3
      87.        21.        14.         3.
       6.        60.         1.        29.
      24.         8.        93.        24.
      11.        38.        14.       128.
      75.        24.        12.        14.
      17.        46.         2.        31.
      44.        16.        58.        31.
      17.        49.        25.       100.
```

```
*      XEQ
*      LABEL
CCOHEN
C      TABLES FOR CHANGE + RESPONSE UNCERTAINTY   COHEN  DATA
       DIMENSION X(35), TT(35), TD(35)
       DIMENSION P(35)
       DIMENSION NACT(33,36,2), P10(35),P1T(35),P11T(35)
       DIMENSION NS(2)
       NX=1
       NP=2
       NR=36
C       ABOVE CARD IS FOR COHENS DATA ALONE
       DO 10 K=1,2
       READ INPUT TAPE 5,102,NS(K)
   102 FORMAT (I4)
       NSI=NS(K)
       WRITE OUTPUT TAPE 6,105,NSI
   105 FORMAT (/I4/)
       DO 10 I=1,NSI
       READ INPUT TAPE 5,100, (NACT(I,J,K),J=1,NR)
       WRITE OUTPUT TAPE 6,100, (NACT(I,J,K),J=1,NR)
   100 FORMAT (4X 43I1)
    10 CONTINUE
       READ INPUT TAPE 5,102,NQ
       DO 33 JK=1,NQ
       READ INPUT TAPE 5,103,NF,NL
       WRITE OUTPUT TAPE 6,103,NF,NL
       NV=NL-1
       NN=NL-NF
       DO 21 NPROB=NX,NP
       DO 15 L=1,NN
       TT(L)=0.
       TD(L)=0.
       P1O(L)=0.
       P1T(L)=0.
       P11T(L)=0.
       P(L)=0.
    15 CONTINUE
       NSI=NS(NPROB)
       DO 12 I=1,NSI
       DO 12 JV=NF,NV
       JK=NL-JV
       J=JV
       DO 11 JJ=1,JK
       K=J+JJ
       P(JJ)=P(JJ)+1.
       TEMP=NACT(I,J,NPROB)
       P1O(JJ)=P10(JJ)+TEMP
       TEMP=NACT(I,K,NPROB)
       P1T(JJ)=P1T(JJ)+TEMP
       TJ=NACT(I,J,NPROB) +NACT(I,K,NPROB)    -1
       IF (TJ) 11,11,13
    13 CONTINUE
       P11T(JJ)=P11T(JJ)+TJ
    11 CONTINUE
    12 CONTINUE
       DO 20 K=1,NN
       TEMP3=P10(K)
       TEMP4=P1T(K)
       TEMP5=P11T(K)
```

```
      P11T(K)=P11T(K)/P(K)
      P1T(K)=P1T(K)/P(K)
      P1C(K)=P10(K)/P(K)
      TEMP =P11T(K)-P1T(K)*P10(K)
      TEMP2 =LOGF(TEMP)
      WRITE OUTPUT TAPE 6,101, P10(K), P1T(K), P11T(K), K,TEMP2,P(K),
     1TEMP3,TEMP4,TEMP5
      X(K)=K
      IF (NPROB-1) 30,30,32
   32 CONTINUE
      TD(K)=-TEMP2
      GO TO 20
   30 CONTINUE
      TT(K)=-TEMP2
   20 CONTINUE
   21 CONTINUE
C    CALLING SEQUENCE IS
C       CALL PPLOT(NSP,X1,Y1,X2,Y2,K,Y1MAX,Y1MIN,Y2MAX,Y2MIN)
C          NSP=NO. OF SAMPLE POINTS
C       X1= FIRST X-ARRAY
C     Y1= FIRST DEPENDENT ARRAY
C    X2= SECOND X-ARRAY
C     Y2=SECOND DEPENDENT ARRAY
C     K=1 FOR COMMON SCALES
C        =C FOR INDEPENDENT SCALES
C     YMAX=MAX VALUE OF Y1
C     Y1MIN=MIN VALUE OF Y1
C    Y2MAX=MAX VALUE OF Y2
C       Y2MIN = MIN VALUE OF Y2
C       IF MAX AND MIN ARE EQUAL, THEN SCALING IS AUTOMATICALLY DNOE FOR
C            MAXIMUM DISPLAY
      WRITE OUTPUT TAPE 6,902
      CALL PPLOT (NN,X,TT,X,TD,C,4.,0.,4.,0.)
      WRITE OUTPUT TAPE 6,902
      CALL PPLOT (NN,X,TT,X,TD,0,4.,2.,4.,2.)
  902 FORMAT (1H1)
   33 CONTINUE
  103 FORMAT (2I3)
      CALL EXIT
  101 FORMAT (3F10.5,I4,F10.7,4F7.0)
      END
*     DATA
  33 NS
202 111111111111111111101111111111111111
203 1000CC1C0C00000000000100C000000000000
205 1111CC111C001111011111111111111111111
206 110010000100000C001000000000000C0000
207 111111111111111111111111111111111111
208 1101110100C00000C00000000000C00000000
209 111111111111111111111111111111111111
210 1001C00000000000100000000000000000000
211 111111111111111110111111111111111111
212 111111101110111111111111111111111111
213 1111C1111111111111111111111111111111
214 1011C1011C10101111101000010101110100
215 111111111110111111111101111111111111
216 111111111111111111111111111111111111
217 1101C11101111001100000011010000000000
219 110011011111101000110110110001110111
220 101101101110101110101111110101111011
```

```
221 111111100000111000100000000000000000
222 111111101111011011111111111111111111
223 101111001010001011111000001101011111
224 111111111111111111111111111111111111
225 111111111111111111111111111111111111
226 111101010100011000010010001000001000
227 111110011011011001110110001010000000
228 111111111111111111111111111111111111
229 101111101011101110101100010001111000
230 110000000000000000000000000000000000
231 111111111111111111111111111111111111
232 111111111111111111111111111111111111
233 101011100111100010110000010101100001
234 111111111111111111111111111111111111
235 111111111111111111111111111111111111
236 110011001111011101011110111111110111
  27   NS
301 100000010000000000000101010000000000
302 111111111111111011001000101111111111
303 111001100011111111111111111111110111
304 111101111011111111111111110111111111
305 111111111111111111111111111111111111
306 101101110110100011011111111111111111
307 111011111111111111111111111111111111
308 001100101111101101111111111111111111
309 111111111111111111111111111111111111
310 100101111111111111111111111111111111
311 101100000010000011010001100100110111
312 111111111111111111111111111111111111
313 101100111111101111111111111111111111
314 110110111111111111111111111111111111
315 111111111111111111111111111111111111
316 111011001010111001111111110111111111
317 101000001010101000000000000000000000
318 101000000000000000000000000000000000
320 111111111111111101111110111111111111
321 111111111111111111111111101111111111
323 100000000000100000000001000000000110
324 111111111111111111111111111111111111
325 111111111111111111101111111111111111
326 111111111111111111111111111111111111
327 001111001111111111111111111111111111
328 111110111111111111111111111111111111
330 001111111111111111111111111111111111
    5      NQ
  1 36      NF,NL
  1 12      NF,NL
  1 18
 19 36
 13 36
```

```
*      XEQ
*      LABEL
CBAYES
C       BAYES THEOREM FOR RESPONSE PATTERNS
C      P1E IS MEAN, C IS CONTAGION PARAMETER, TK IS MOVEMENT FROM DICHOT
       DIMENSION X(101), FNN(101),FNT(101)
       DIMENSION FNR(36),TM(36),PIR(101), P(101),FNQ(36,102),TP(101)
       DIMENSION FNW(36,101)
       DEC1=0.
       N=100
       NP=N+1
       NPP=NP+1
       READ INPUT TAPE 5,100,NPROB
       READ INPUT TAPE 5,100, NR
       NRP=NR+1
       DO 51 NV=1,NPROB
       READ INPUT TAPE 5,101,P1E,C,TK
       WRITE OUTPUT TAPE 6,104,P1E,C, TK
       DO 10 I=1,NP
       X(I)=I-1
       P(I)=0.
   10  CONTINUE
       CALL PROP(P1E,C,NP,P,DEC1)
C      CALCULATE EXPECTED CHANGE AT LEVEL OF INDIVIDUAL.
C      TIME PERIOD IS IN UNITS EQUAL TO TIME BETWEEN 2ND AND 3RD OBSERV.
       DVP=0.
       DVN=0.
       DO 193 I=1,NP
       TP=I-1
       TX=N
       TP=TP/TX
       TEMP=(P1E-TP)*P(I)
       IF (TEMP) 191,191,192
  191  DVN=DVN+TK*TEMP
       GO TO 193
  192  DVP=DVP+TK*TEMP
  193  CONTINUE
       DELTV=DVP-DVN
       WRITE OUTPUT TAPE 6,740, DVP,DVN,DELTV
       CALL PPLOT (NP,X,P,X,P,0,.1,0.,.1,0.)
       DO 9 I=1,NRP
       FNR(I)=1.
    9  CONTINUE
       DO 11 NI=1,NR
       FNQ(NI,NPP)=0.
       FI=NR-NI+1
       FJ =NI
       FNR(NI+1) =FNR(NI)*FI/FJ
   11  CONTINUE
       TN =N
       DO 13 I=1,NP
       TI =I-1
       TP(I)=(TI/TN)
   13  CONTINUE
       DO 14 NI=1,NRP
       TM(NI)=0.
       DO 15 I=1,NP
       FNQ(NI,I) =FNR(NI)*TP(I)**(NI-1)*(1.-TP(I))**(NRP-NI)
       FNW(NI,I)=FNQ(NI,I)
   15  CONTINUE
```

```
  14 CONTINUE
     FNQ(1,1)=1.
     FNQ(NRP,NP)=1.
     DO 21 NI=1,NRP
     DO 21 I=1,NP
     FNQ(NI,I) =FNQ(NI,I)*P(I)
     TM(NI)=TM(NI) + FNQ(NI,I)
  21 CONTINUE
     DO 16 I=1,NP
     DO 17 NI=1,NRP
     FNQ(NI,I)=FNQ(NI,I)/TM(NI)
     FNQ(NI,NPP)=FNQ(NI,NPP) + FNQ(NI,I)
  17 CONTINUE
  16 CONTINUE
     DO 19 NI=1,NRP,2
     NJ=NI+1
     NII=NI-1
     NJJ=NJ-1
     WRITE OUTPUT TAPE 6,103
     WRITE OUTPUT TAPE 6,102,NII,  (FNQ(NI,I),I=1,NPP)
     WRITE OUTPUT TAPE 6,102,NJJ,  (FNQ(NJ,I),I=1,NPP)
     DO 20 K=1,NP
     FNN(K)=FNQ(NI,K)
     FNT(K)=FNQ(NI+1,K)
  20 CONTINUE
     CALL PPLOT(NP,X,FNN,X,FNT,0,.1,0.,.1,0.)
  19 CONTINUE
  51 CONTINUE
     CALL EXIT
 100 FORMAT (I3)
 101 FORMAT (F10.9,F10.5,F10.5)
 102 FORMAT (1XI3,/(1X20F6.4))
 103 FORMAT (1H1)
 104 FORMAT (1XF10.9,F10.5,F10.5)
 740 FORMAT (/1X 29HAV. INDIV. CHANGE POSITIVE = ,F7.4,11HNEGATIVE = ,
    1F7.4, 8HTOTAL = ,F7.4 /)
     END
*    DATA
  1  NPROB
  1  NR
.650          2.68        .01      P10,C,TK
```

Bibliography

Anderson, T. W., and L. A. Goodman, 1957, "Statistical Inference About Markov Chains," *Ann. Math. Stat.*, **28,** 89–110.

Asch, S. E., 1951, "Effect of Group Pressure upon the Modification and Distortion of Judgments," in *Groups, Leadership, and Men*, Harold Guetzkow, ed. (Pittsburgh: Carnegie Press).

Bartlett, M. S., 1955, *An Introduction to Stochastic Processes* (London: Cambridge University Press).

Bharucha-Reid, A. T., 1960, *Elements of the Theory of Markov Processes and Their Applications* (New York: McGraw-Hill Book Company), p. 215, #A.4.

Blumen, I., M. Kogan, and P. J. McCarthy, 1955, *The Industrial Mobility of Labor as a Probability Process* (Ithaca, N.Y.: Cornell University Press).

Bush, R. R., and F. Mosteller, 1955, *Stochastic Modes for Learning* (New York: John Wiley & Sons, Inc.).

Cohen, Bernard, 1963, *Conflict and Conformity* (Cambridge: Massachusetts Institute of Technology Press).

Coleman, J. S., 1962, "Reward Structures and the Allocation of Effort," in *Mathematical Methods in Small Group Processes*, Joan H. Criswell, Herbert Solomon, and Patrick Suppes, eds. (Stanford, Calif.: Stanford University Press), pp. 119–132.

———, 1964, *Introduction to Mathematical Sociology* (New York: The Free Press of Glencoe, Inc.).

Converse, Philip, 1962, "The Nature of Belief Systems in Mass Publics," mimeographed (Ann Arbor, Mich.: Survey Research Center).

Feller, William, 1943, "On a General Class of 'Contagious' Distributions," *Ann. Math. Stat.*, **14,** 389–400.

———, 1951, "Diffusion Processes in Genetics," *Proc. 2nd Berkeley Symposium on Math. Stat. and Probability*, 227–246.

———, 1957, *An Introduction to Probability Theory and Its Applications*, 2nd ed. (New York: John Wiley & Sons, Inc.).

Fourt, Louis, 1960, "Applying Markov Chain Analysis to NCP Brand Switching Data," mimeographed (New York: Market Research Corporation of America).

Frank, Ronald, 1962, "Brand Choice as a Probability Process," *J. of Bus.*, **35.**

Goodman, Leo A., 1959, "On Some Statistical Tests for M-th Order Markov Chains," *Ann. Math. Stat.*, **30,** 154–164.

———, 1961, "Statistical Methods for the Mover-Stayer Model," *J. Amer. Stat. Assoc.*, **56,** 841–868.

Kuehn, Alfred A., 1958, "An Analysis of the Dynamics of Consumer Behavior and Its Implications for Marketing Management," unpublished Ph.D. dissertation (Pittsburgh: Carnegie Institute of Technology).

———, 1962, chapter in *Quantitative Techniques in Marketing Analysis*, R. E. Frank, A. A. Kuehn, and W. F. Massey, eds. (Homewood, Ill.: Richard D. Irwin, Inc.).

Lazarsfeld, Paul F., 1959, "Latent Structure Analysis," in *Psychology: A Study of a Science, Conceptual and Systematic*, Vol. III, Sigmund Koch, ed. (New York: McGraw-Hill Book Company), pp. 476–543.

———, 1961, "The Algebra of Dichotomous Systems," *Studies in Item Analysis and Prediction*, Herbert Solomon, ed. (Stanford, Calif: Stanford University Press).

Levenson, Bernard, 1963, personal communication.

McDill, Edward L., and J. S. Coleman, 1963, "High School Social Status, College Plans, Interest in Academic Achievement: A Panel Analysis," *Amer. Soc. Rev.*, **28,** 905–918.

Tainiter, M., 1962, "An Application of a Markovian Model to the Prediction of the Reliability of Electronic Circuits," mimeographed (Yorktown Heights, N.Y.: IBM Research Center).

Wiggins, Lee M., 1955, "Mathematical Models for the Interpretation of Attitude and Behavior Change: The Analysis of Multi-Wave Panels," unpublished Ph.D. dissertation (New York: Columbia University).

Index